FLYING WITH THE
AVIDYNE IFD

Third Edition

for AviOS 10.3.0.2

Michael F . Bauer
& Avidyne

ISBN 979-8-218-00965-6

Published by:

Avidyne Corporation
www.avidyne.com

REV10.3.0.2 September 12, 2022

Acknowledgements

Avidyne and the entire pilot community mourn the loss of our friend, author, and trusted Avidyne Pilot, Michael F. Bauer. Michael wrote this book "Flying the Avidyne IFD" that we continue to use to help our new pilots learn the Avidyne systems. We honor him with the publication of this new edition, which he had started editing prior to his passing in February 2022.

Fly with the Angels, Michael!

Special thanks to Patricia Schroeder, Michael's partner and collaborator.

Thanks also to Mike Salmon and Jim Flattery for their assistance in marking up and proof reading this 3rd edition of the book. - Tom Harper, Avidyne

Contents

Intentionally Left Blank

Introduction

The Avidyne IFD series is a family of aviation GPS/NAV/COM navigators manufactured by Avidyne Corporation of Melbourne, FL. It includes the IFD550, IFD545, IFD540, IFD510, IFD440, and IFD410 products. "IFD" stands for "Integrated Flight Display." This means that, in a single panel-mounted box, each IFD can incorporate a traditional VHF navigation and communication radio, a GPS navigator, an airline-quality flight management system (FMS), a terrain awareness and alerting, and a Multi-Function Display (MFD) capable of displaying a moving map with navigation data, traffic, weather, and approach charts.

That is a great deal of functionality to be packed into a single unit. In order to use it all effectively you, the pilot, must be thoroughly trained and familiar with all facets of IFD operation.

That is where this book comes in. It is a structured course that will teach you how to operate your IFD effectively. It is divided into a series of lessons, starting with simple operations and proceeding to more complex ones. They will lead you through the most important things that you can do with your IFD.

The course will not teach you every way to perform every function. (Like most computers, the IFDs have lots of ways to do most things.) And it does not talk about some of the "cool features" available in the navigators. Instead, this course is designed to teach you how to use the Avidyne units effectively in the most common flight situations. We will show you at least one way to do the most important things that you need to do. That will give you the foundation you need to understand the basics. When you have finished the course you will be able to understand the Avidyne IFD Pilot Guides and will be able to explore further details and features on your own.

Structure of This Course

This course is divided into eleven individual lessons which explore different facets of IFD operations.

Each lesson is based around a scenario, a real life flight that you could undertake with your IFD. You will use Avidyne's free play IFD Trainer App to practice each flight on your iPad tablet. The combination of the structured lessons and the simulator will give you familiarity with the IFD navigators. You will know where everything is and develop good habit patterns before you ever get into a real airplane.

The lessons are:

- Lesson 1: Introducing the Avidyne IFD Navigators

  A basic overview of the IFD product line, showing the panel layout and introducing all the knobs and buttons.

- Lesson 2: The Avidyne IFD Trainer App/ IFDSimulator

  How to obtain, install, and operate Avidyne's IFD Trainer App.

- Lesson 3: The Communication and Navigation Radios

  Conventional navigation and communication with VHF nav/com radios.

- Lesson 4: Building and Flying a Simple Flight Plan

  Introduction to GPS navigation and flight plans using the FMS.

- Lesson 5: Changing a Flight Plan

  How to add and delete flight plan waypoints, go direct to a waypoint, and change your destination.

- Lesson 6: Advanced Flight Plans

  Using airways, standard arrivals and departures, radial interceptions, and course offsets in flight plans.

- Lesson 7: Saving and Re-Using Flight Plans

  Saving a flight plan for later use and retrieving it when you need it.

- Lesson 8: Holding Patterns

  How to program and fly a random or charted holding pattern.

- Lesson 9: Approaches

  How to add an Instrument approach and execute it successfully.

  How to add a Visual Approach and execute it successfully.

- Lesson 10: Information and Utilities

  Sources of information built into your IFD navigator, including databases, calculators, and timers.

- Lesson 11: Pilot Settings and Options

  How to customize your IFD to make it look and act the way you want it to.

As complete as these lessons are, they are not enough by themselves. They give you the fundamentals of flying with the IFDs. But you will also need time with an instructor in a real aircraft to become truly proficient in using these products. The real aircraft is the only place to experience how the Avidyne units work with the other equipment in your airplane and understand how they perform in actual flight.

CAUTION: Do not attempt actual IFR operation on the basis of this book alone. Always practice in VFR conditions with an instructor or a safety pilot before you use your IFD in actual instrument conditions.

Going through the course lessons in this book will give you the foundation that you need, and will make your aircraft training far more effective than it would be if you flew the airplane with no prior preparation. But this course only supplements aircraft training with a CFII; it can never replace it.

Note: For simplicity's sake the lessons in this book will all focus on the IFD540. However, the features and procedures introduced will work on all the models in the IFD line. Specific differences will be noted when they are necessary.

Course Supplement Materials

This book does not stand alone. It should be used with other materials to give you a complete picture of IFD operations. supplemental training videos for each of these lessons are available at www.avidyne.com

The most important of these are the Avidyne IFD Pilot Guides, published by Avidyne and available in PDF format for download at no charge at www.avidyne.com. These are the reference books which give you every detail of the navigators. They contain far more information than can be included in this course, and they will be revised if new software introduces new features. Always refer to them for details and final answers. This book is not intended as a replacement for the Avidyne Pilot's Guides, but rather a high-level overview of the basic operations of your IFD in a scenario-based format.

You should also become familiar with the IFD Flight Manual Supplement for your aircraft. This document is prepared specifically for your individual installation. It contains limitations, operating information, and emergency procedures for your aircraft. You should carry it in your aircraft and incorporate it into your everyday flying.

The Instrument Procedures Handbook, published by the FAA and available at www.faa.gov, provides a good reference for general IFR flight and GPS/WAAS operations. Every instrument pilot should be familiar with it.

For a more detailed look at GPS, WAAS, and how the system works consult the GPS and WAAS Instrument Flying Handbook by Max Trescott (www.glasscockpitbooks.com). It will give you the finer points of the GPS and WAAS systems, how GPS/WAAS approaches are built, and how to fly them.

And, as always, the final authority on airspace and IFR operations is the Aeronautical Information Manual, available from the FAA at www.faa.gov.

Intentionally Left Blank

Lesson 1: Introducing the Avidyne IFD Navigators

This lesson introduces you to the Avidyne IFD family of FMS/GPS/NAV/COM systems. It will tell you about the unit's controls and give you a basic introduction to the front panel layout of the IFDs. At the end of this lesson you will understand the basic components and will be ready to begin the next lessons, which will explore the units in detail.

Introduction

The Avidyne IFD FMS/GPS/NAV/COM units are designed to give a pilot centralized control for communi-cations, navigation, computer-based flight planning, and fuel management. They also can display optional weather and traffic information. Each IFD is a single Integrated Flight Display (IFD) unit. Either one or two IFDs can be mounted in an aircraft, in any combination. When more than one IFD is installed, the units work together to provide support and added functionality for each other.

All the IFD units contain the following components:

- Full color touch screen display with moving map

- Control knobs

- Function control keys & Line Select Keys (LSKs)

- Page function rocker switches

- Navigation and Flight Management System (FMS)

- Global Positioning System (GPS) navigation sensor which includes a satellite-based augmentation system (WAAS in the US)

- 3D Synthetic Vision (and Terrain Awareness & Alerting)

- Navigation database

- Terrain and obstacle databases

- Approach Chart & Airport Diagram database (IFD550, IFD545, IFD540 and IFD100 only)

- Optional datalink weather and traffic display

- VOR and ILS (VLOC) navigation sensor (except IFD545, IFD510, and IFD410)

- VHF communications radios (except IFD545, IFD510, and IFD410)

The members of the Avidyne IFD product line are:

IFD540

The IFD 540 is considered to be the core member of the IFD family. It includes all the features listed above and has a large 5.7 inch (diagonal) touch screen with 640x480 resolution.

IFD550

The IFD550 has all the features of the IFD540. In addition, it includes a solid-state attitude reference system (ARS). This enables it to display an on-screen attitude indicator which includes egocentric 3D synthetic vision.

IFD440

The IFD440 is a smaller version of the IFD540. It is two inches shorter and includes a 4.8 inch (diagonal), 640x235 touch screen instead of the larger 5.7 inch screen on the IFD540.

IFD545

The IFD545 is a GPS navigation-only version of the IFD550. It does not include VHF navigation or communications radios.

IFD510

The IFD510 is a GPS navigation-only version of the IFD540. It does not include VHF navigation or communications radios.

IFD410

The IFD410 is a GPS navigation-only version of the IFD440. It does not include VHF navigation or communications radios

The rest of this course will refer to all of the IFD units as the **IFD5XX/4XX** or simply the **IFD**. Since much of the functionality is the same for all, the lessons will be based on the IFD540. Its screen is larger and easier to work with than that of the IFD440. The difference between the IFD540 and other IFD units is described in a **Differences** section at the end of each lesson. All references to the IFD540 pertain to the IFD550 as well.

The following figures show the Avidyne IFD550, IFD540 and IFD440.

Figure 1 - 1 The Avidyne IFD550

Lesson 1: Introducing the Avidyne IFD Navigators

Figure 1 - 2 The Avidyne IFD540

Figure 1 - 3 The Avidyne IFD440

Hybrid Touch Operation

The IFD units are operated using "hybrid touch" technology. That means that you can perform most functions using the control knobs and buttons, the touch screen, or a combination of the two. The hybrid touch philosophy makes it easy to use the IFDs in rough air or turbulence, where you can grab a knob or press a key but it's hard to touch a screen in the right place. It gives you flexibility to use the units in whatever manner is most convenient at the time. But hybrid touch increases the complexity of the IFD units because there are several different ways to accomplish almost any task.

To use the IFDs effectively you do not need to know every possible way to perform every single function. You only need to know one way to perform each. It is also helpful to know a "knob" method and a "touch screen" method. Therefore, this manual will show a variety of techniques. But remember – one is usually enough. Pick whichever method you like best.

Lesson 1: Introducing the Avidyne IFD Navigators

Navigation

The IFD "knows" where it is at all times by receiving GPS information. It continuously monitors the quality of the GPS signal to ensure that it is adequate for accurate navigation. The IFD550, IFD540, and IFD440 also include conventional VOR and ILS navigation receivers, which are referred to as "VLOC" (VOR-Localizer) sensors.

The unit's built-in navigation database contains waypoints, navaids, and airports. It also contains standard departures, standard arrivals, instrument approaches, and airways. You can add additional waypoints of your own to the database. AviOS 10.3 and later adds programmable Visual Approach guidance.

You can program the IFD to execute complete flight plans, including airways, holding patterns, and instrument approaches. When you couple a GPSS-equipped autopilot to the IFD the aircraft will automatically follow the twists and turns of any flight plan.

Display and Controls

At first glance, the IFD has an imposing number of buttons and knobs. It will be much easier to understand them if they are divided into a few major groupings, given below.

These descriptions are only intended to give you a basic, "big-picture" understanding of the IFD's controls. Full details will be provided in later lessons.

The IFD's major components are:

The Display Screen and Page Function Keys

The **Display Screen** is the most prominent feature on the IFD. It can be used to show a moving map, as well as a wide variety of navigational and flight planning information. It is touch-sensitive so you can tap and "drag" it to perform many functions.

Figure 1 - 4 The IFD Display Screen

Lesson 1: Introducing the Avidyne IFD Navigators

The information on the display is divided into several pages. You can select which page is shown by using the **Page Function Keys**, located under the display. There are three of them, labeled **FMS**, **MAP**, and **AUX**.

Each page is divided into several different **Tabs**, located at the bottom of the display. The number and function of the tabs are different for each page.

The page function keys are "rocker" switches, meaning that each can be pressed in the center or on the right or left side. Pressing a page function key in the center brings up the page associated with it, pressing it again on the right or left side moves between the tabs on the bottom of the page. You can also select a tab by simply touching it on the screen.

Figure 1 - 5 Page Function Keys and Page Tabs

The Control Keys

There are several control keys on the right and left side of the IFD. They include the following:

The **Line Select Keys** (LSKs) are on the left side of the IFD. Their functions are "context sensitive," which means that each key does not do one specific thing. Its function will change according to what page or tab is being shown. The action of each line select key can be determined at any time by looking at the **Caption** immediately to the right of the key.

The **Frequency Swap Key** exchanges the active and standby communication or navigation radio frequency.

The **Dedicated Function Keys** are located to the right of the display. They are "shortcuts" to specific IFD functions.

Two of the dedicated function keys are particularly important:

- The **ENTR** key is generally used to accept an item of data that you have entered with the knobs or on-screen keyboard.

> **Note:** Pressing the center of the IFD Multi-Function knob is equivalent to pressing the **ENTR** key. This is often convenient because you can use a "twist and push" sequence when you use the knob to enter data.
>
> The lessons in the course will always tell you to press the **ENTR** key, but remember that you can also push the **IFD Multi-Function** knob instead.

- The **CLR** key is an "undo" key. It can be used to cancel a previous selection or delete items from a flight plan.

Figure 1 - 6 IFD Keys

The Knobs

The four knobs located in the corners of the IFD are:

The **Volume/Power/Squelch/ID Knob** is in the upper left corner of the IFD. It controls the volume and the mode or squelch of whichever navigation or communication radio is selected. It can also be used to power off the IFD, although this function is rarely used. The IFD is normally powered up automatically when the aircraft avionics bus is powered.

The **COM/VLOC Knob** is in the lower left corner of the IFD. It is used to tune the frequency of the selected navigation or communications radio.

The **CDI Nav Source Knob** is located on the upper right corner of the IFD. It controls the source of the navigation information.

The right bottom knob is the **IFD Multi-Function Knob**. It is used for many purposes, determined by which page is being shown on the display. In each case, the action of the knob is shown by the label that appears on the display above and to the left of the knob. As discussed above, the center of the knob can be pressed in to perform the same function as the ENTR key.

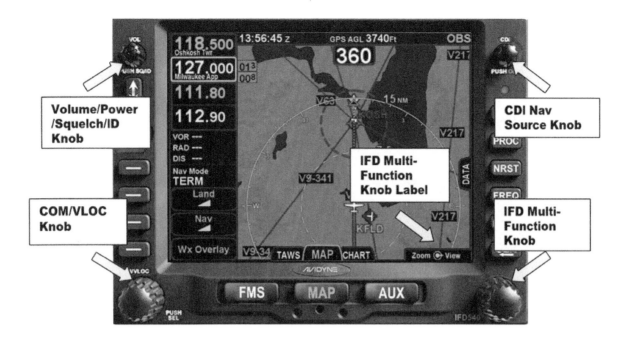

Figure 1 - 7 IFD Knobs

The On-Screen Keyboard

A keyboard can be displayed on the IFD's touch-sensitive display screen, as shown in the figure below. It can be used to enter waypoint identifiers and other alphanumeric information.

Figure 1 - 8 On-Screen Keyboard

The Wireless Keyboard

Avidyne also offers the MK10 Bluetooth wireless keyboard for use with the IFD navigators. It can be used in place of the on-screen keyboard.

Figure 1 - 9 MK10 Wireless Keyboard

IFD440 Differences

The IFD440 has the same functionality as the IFD540. The main difference is that it is smaller, so it takes up less space in your avionics panel. This means that it can't show as much information or have as many controls as the IFD540.

The differences between the IFD540 and IFD440 are:

- The display screen of the IFD440 is not as tall.

- The IFD440 only has three line select keys, instead of four on the IFD540. All of the functions controlled by the missing keys are still available on the IFD440. But they can't be accessed directly by a single key press from the front panel. You have to go through a menu to reach them.

- The IFD440 only has four dedicated function keys (Direct, PROC, ENTR, and CLR) instead of six (Direct, PROC, NRST, FREQ, ENTR, and CLR) on the IFD540. The functions on the two keys that are not included on the IFD440 are still available. They must be accessed through the FMS pages, not directly from the front panel.

- The IFD440 cannot be used to display approach charts.

IFD545, IFD510, and IFD410 Differences

The IFD545, IFD510, and IFD410 do not include VHF navigation (VLOC) or communication radios. Therefore, they do not have the Volume/Power/Squelch/ID and COM/VLOC knobs which are on the left side of the other IFD units. An ON/OFF push button is located in the upper left corner of the three units.

IFD550 Differences

The IFD550 has an additional page function key, labeled **SVS**. It is used to control the 3D synthetic vision feature.

Lesson 1: Introducing the Avidyne IFD Navigators

Lesson 2: The Avidyne IFD Simulator

The exercises in this book rely heavily on Avidyne's IFD simulator program, which is called the **IFD Trainer**. It is an excellent learning tool which will make your transition to the IFD5XX/4XX much easier. For home simulators, Avidyne also offers IFD Trainer XP, the companion app for the X-Plane flight simulator.

This lesson will show you how to install, configure, and operate the IFD simulator program. It will provide the foundation you need to start the training scenarios. At the end of this lesson you will have successfully installed the simulator on your iPad and will know how to use it for the lessons that follow.

> **Note:** The IFD Trainer program runs only on an Apple iPad. You must have an iPad to use the trainer.

Introduction

Avidyne provides a full-featured simulator for its IFD products. The simulator is based on the same computer code that runs on the actual hardware installed in your airplane. It operates the same as the actual units, except that it operates with an iPad screen instead of the knobs and buttons on the real units.

As realistic as the IFD Trainer is, it does have its limitations. Most importantly: the simulator is a stand-alone implementation of the IFD5XX/4XX. It does not have the connections to other equipment (such as navigation indicators, HSIs, autopilots, audio panels, or external sensors) that you would have in a real airplane. The simulator will accurately follow any flight plan you program into it, but will not follow the descent profile of an instrument approach. It cannot be used as stand-alone learning tool because it doesn't completely simulate the environment of a real airplane.

This does not mean that the simulator isn't valuable. It is extremely helpful because it allows you to familiarize yourself with the nuances of the IFD5XX/4XX without the time and expense of using a real aircraft. It allows you to perform all the practice scenarios in this book, and it allows you to pause the action. You can also make up your own scenarios, tailored to the kind of flying that you do. The simulator lets you set up and practice multiple scenarios in different parts of the country, something you could never do in an airplane without hours of flying. You can preview flights and approaches before you attempt to fly them in real life, making trips to new airports as familiar as local flights.

Installing and Configuring the IFD Trainer App

Installation

The IFD Trainer can be found on Apple's App Store. Use the following procedure to install it.

- ☑ Go to the **App Store** on your iPad.
- ☑ Use the search box to search for **Avidyne**.
- ☑ Tap on the **IFD Trainer** cloud symbol or GET button.
- ☑ The simulator will download and install itself automatically.

☑ Tap on the **OPEN** button to start the simulator for the first time.

Figure 2 - 1 The Avidyne IFD Trainer on the App Store

☑ The first time you open the simulator it will display a registration screen. At the same time, it will download and install a terrain database. Progress of the terrain download is shown at the bottom of the screen.

☑ Type your registration information into the screen and wait for the download indicator to reach 100%.

☑ When the terrain download has been completed, tap on **Start** on the bottom left corner of the screen.

☑ A **What's New** screen may appear. Tap on the red X in the top right corner to close it.

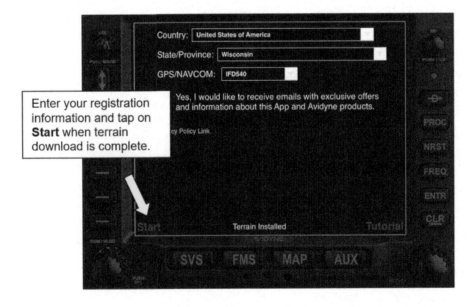

Figure 2 - 2 The Registration Screen

Lesson 2: The Avidyne IFD simulator

Installing the Simulator's Databases

When the simulator starts it will display the bezel of an IFD550 navigator. Before you can use it you must install the appropriate aeronautical databases. Use the following procedure:

☑ Tap on the **Databases** menu on the top of the simulator screen.

☑ A menu of two possible databases will be displayed. They are:

- The **Demonstration** database: This is a free database that is included with the simulator. It does not get revisions and changes infrequently.

- The **Jeppesen** database: This database is available to Jeppesen subscribers. It does receive revision service.

> **Note:** All the exercises in this book are based on the demonstration databases. If you download the Jeppesen database, you may not see the same navigational fixes that are used here. The exercises may not match the demonstration database exactly if revisions have been made since the exercises were developed.

☑ Tap on **Demonstration Databases**. A dialog box will appear. Tap on **OK**.

☑ A Jeppesen database download page will appear. Tap on the cloud symbol next to **NavData**, then tap on **Download**. The worldwide navigation database will be downloaded.

☑ Use the same procedure to download the **Obstacles** and **eCharts** databases.

☑ Tap on **Exit** when your downloads are complete.

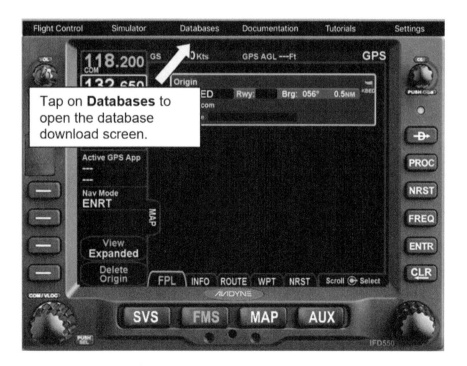

Figure 2 - 3 The Initial Simulator Screen

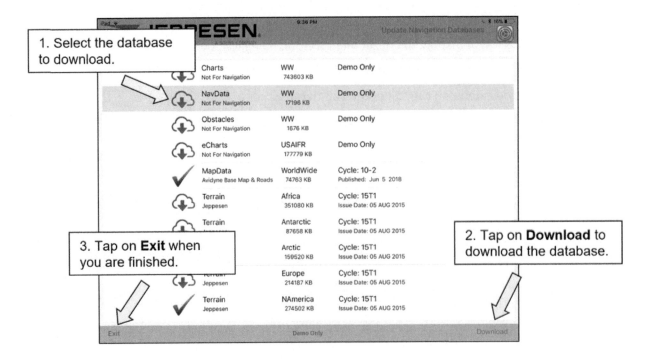

Figure 2 - 4 The Database Download Screen

Configuring the Simulator

The final step is to configure the simulator for the type of IFD device you want to use. Do the following:

☑ Open the iPad's **Settings** app.

☑ On the left side of the screen, scroll down to and tap on **IFD Trainer.**

☑ On the right side of the screen, you can select two IFD Trainer settings. They are:

- **Aircraft Type:** This controls the aircraft symbol that is displayed on the IFD's moving map. The possible selections are Fixwing, Helicopter, and Jet.

- **Device Type:** This controls the type of IFD device that the simulator will display.

> **Note:** All the exercises in this book use the IFD540 version of the simulator. The differences between it and the other IFD units are explained in each lesson.

Starting and Operating the Simulator

Starting the Simulator

☑ Start the simulator by tapping on its icon.

Figure 2 - 5 The IFD Trainer Icon

Simulator Menus

There are six menu options located on the top of the simulator screen. Tap on any one of them to select it. The menus are:

1. **Flight Control**

    The **Flight Control** menu allows you to control how the simulator is flown. Its options are:

    • **Follow FPL:** The simulator will follow the flight plan that is loaded in the IFD. This is like flying with an autopilot in the NAV mode. A slider bar will appear at the bottom of the simulator screen. It allows you to control the simulated aircraft's airspeed.

    • **Autopilot:** The simulator will fly as if it were connected to an autopilot in the HDG mode. Slider bars will appear that will allow you to control the simulated aircraft's airspeed, heading, and altitude.

    • **Manual:** A manual "stick" icon will be displayed. It allows you to control the pitch and roll of the simulator manually.

    > **Note:** All the exercises in this book assume that the simulator is in **Follow FPL** mode.

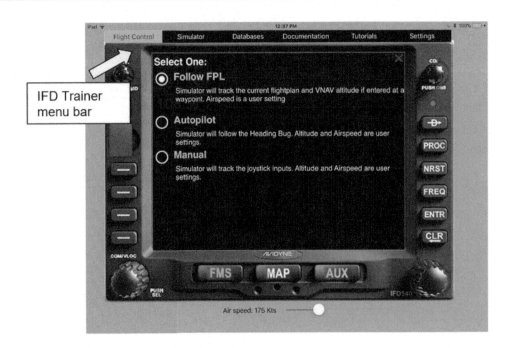

Figure 2 - 6 The Flight Control Menu Page

2. **Simulator** - The **Simulator** menu allows you to control the speed of the simulator. You may pause the simulator, you may have it fly in real time, or you may speed it up by a factor of two or four. This is very useful when you want to fly a long distance in a short time.

3. **Databases** - The **Databases** menu controls the installation of aeronautical databases. (wifi connection required).

4. **Documentation** - The **Documentation** menu can be used to download the IFD pilot's guides and a quick reference guide for the IFD Trainer and IFD 100 apps. (wifi connection required)

5. **Tutorials** - The **Tutorials** menu is used to access video tutorials for the IFD Trainer app and the IFDs themselves. (wifi connection required)

6. **Settings** - The **Settings** menu is where you select which model of IFD you would like to emulate. All six models are available including FMS/GPS/NAV/COMs (IFD550, IFD540, IFD440) and FMS/GPS only models (IFD545, IFD510, and IFD410).

Operation of Buttons and Knobs

Tap on any simulator button to press it. The three bottom buttons are "rockers" and can be pressed on either side.

Small red or blue arrows appear on all four knobs. Drag them to turn the knobs. The blue arrows turn the small knobs; the red arrows turn the large ones.

Figure 2 - 7 IFD Knob Operation

Touch Screen

The simulated screen works just like the touch screen on the real IFD. Tap and scroll it with your finger.

Starting and Repositioning

When the simulator starts it is always positioned at the origin of its previous flight plan. You can reposition it to any airport you'd like by opening the **FPL** tab on the **FMS** page and setting an origin airport. This will be discussed further in Lesson 3.

Airspeed, Altitude and Heading Control

Airspeed is controlled by a slider bar on the bottom of the screen.

Altitude is controlled automatically in the **Follow FPL** mode by entering crossing altitudes in specific waypoints. The simulator will obey them. In **Autopilot** mode altitude is controlled by a slider bar on the right side of the screen.

Time Control

The simulation can be paused or speeded up by using the settings under the **Simulator** menu.

Clearing Alerts

The IFD5XX/4XX presents cyan, yellow, and red alerts in the lower right corner of the screen. These may or may not be relevant, depending on what you're doing with the simulator. Clear them by pressing the simulator's **CLR** key.

Simulated Traffic and Weather

Traffic is displayed all the time on the iPad simulator and can't be turned off. It causes random traffic alerts to be displayed but has no other effects on the simulation.

Simulated weather is displayed in the northeast part of the United States. It simulates the presence of an ADS-B receiver.

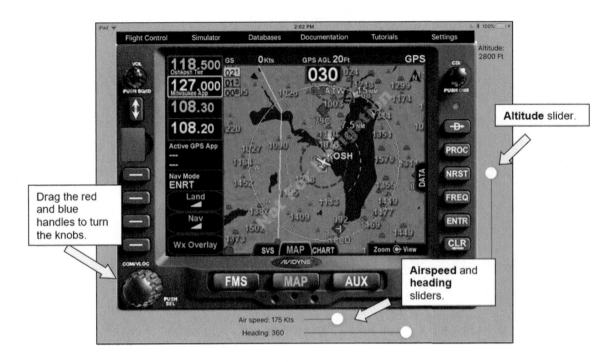

Figure 2 - 8 The iPad Simulator Controls in Autopilot Mode

Lesson Review

This lesson has introduced the installation and operation of the Avidyne IFD Trainer program. The items discussed were:

Simulator Availability

- Avidyne provides an IFD Trainer program which simulates the operation of all the IFD models.

- The simulator runs on an Apple iPad (iOS).

- The simulator uses the same software code that runs on the actual aircraft hardware. It provides a very accurate imitation of the real units.

- The program does not provide a simulation of the aircraft equipment that is typically connected to an IFD5XX/4XX, such as navigation indicators, autopilots, and external sensors.

- The simulator can track the flight plan that has been programmed into an IFD. It can also fly specified headings and altitudes if it is run in Autopilot mode.

- The simulator cannot be used by itself to learn the IFD5XX/4XX. It must always be used in conjunction with practice in an actual airplane.

- Despite its limitations, the simulator is a very effective training tool. It can be used for familiarization with the IFD5XX/4XX and to perform practice scenarios. Its use will greatly reduce cost and enhance the value of aircraft training.

Lesson 2: The Avidyne IFD simulator

Installing and Configuring the Simulator

- The simulator is found on the Apple App store. Search for Avidyne to find it. It is called the IFD Trainer.

- Tapping on the cloud symbol or GET button on the App Store will download and install the simulator.

- The simulator can be configured from the iPad's Settings app.

Operating the IFD Trainer

- The simulator buttons are operated by tapping on them.

- The simulator knobs are rotated by dragging small red and blue arrows.

- The touch screen as operated by tapping and scrolling it directly.

- Alerts will appear in the lower right corner of the screen. Clear them by tapping the CLR key.

- Airspeed, altitude, and simulator movement can be controlled moving sliders on the iPad screen.

- The Flight Control menu is used to control the operation of the simulator. In Follow FPL mode the simulated airplane will follow the programmed flight plan. In Autopilot and Manual modes it can be controlled manually.

- The Simulator menu is used to control the speed of the simulator. It can be paused, run normally, or sped up by a factor of two or four.

Lesson 3: The Communication and Navigation Radios

The IFDs are full-featured GPS navigators and flight management systems. However, they also contain "traditional" VHF communication and VOR/ILS navigation radios. It will be helpful to explore the VHF functions and controls before moving on to the more advanced GPS capabilities.

This lesson will introduce the IFD's VHF navigation and communication capabilities, as well as their controls. At the end of this lesson you will understand how to communicate and to perform traditional VOR/ILS navigation with the IFD5XX/4XX.

> **Note:** This lesson does not apply to the IFD545, IFD510, and IFD410. These devices do not contain VHF navigation or communication capability.

The Scenario

Let's use an exercise to explore how the communications and navigation radios work. Imagine the following:

You have just received a VIP tour of the Avidyne factory in Melbourne, Florida. Your new IFD540 was installed there and your finished aircraft is on the ramp at the Melbourne airport, KMLB.

You plan to ferry your newly-refurbished airplane back to your home base in the Chicago area. You're not familiar with the IFD540's GPS capabilities yet, so you plan to fly VFR and use traditional VOR-based navigation.

Your initial route of flight will take you north to the Ormond Beach VOR (OMN – 112.6). From there you will proceed to the St. Augustine VOR (SGJ – 109.4).

The tower at the Melbourne airport is on frequency 118.2. Ground control is on 121.9.

Tuning the Communications Radio

Your first challenge is to tune the Melbourne tower and ground frequencies so you can taxi out to the runway.

Proceed as follows:

- ☑ Start the IFD540 simulator on your iPad.

- ☑ The **MAP** page may already be displayed, as is shown in the illustration below. If it's not, press the **MAP** rocker to display it.

- ☑ The Melbourne FL airport (KMLB) should be displayed in the middle of the screen. If it's not, reposition the simulator to KMLB using the **Set the Origin Airport** procedure described in Lesson 4.

- ☑ Note the following:

  - The **Frequency Boxes** are located in the upper left corner of the display screen.

  - The top two frequency boxes contain communication frequencies, the bottom two are navigation (VOR/ILS) frequencies.

Note: The frequency boxes shown are Avidyne's default configuration. Your IFD may look different; you can change the display to show more or fewer frequency boxes. This will be explored in a later lesson. If the frequencies do not appear as shown, reset the simulator using the procedure described in the **Returning to the Factory's Default Datablocks** section in Lesson 11.

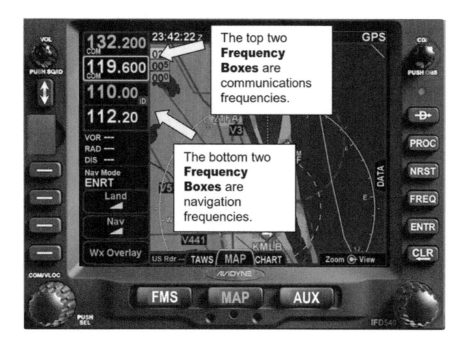

Figure 3 - 1 The IFD Com and Nav Frequency Boxes

- In each frequency pair, the top number is the **Active Frequency**, displayed in green. This is the one you are currently using. The bottom is the **Standby Frequency**. It is waiting for future use and is displayed in white..

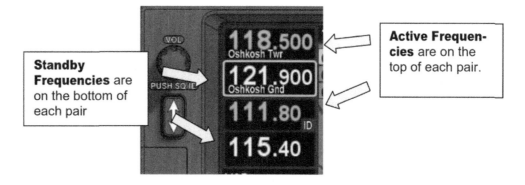

Figure 3 - 2 The Active and Standby Frequencies

- The communications (top) standby frequency is surrounded by a cyan box. This is the **Selected Frequency**. It's the frequency that will be replaced with a new value. The Active frequency cannot be selected directly for tuning.

Lesson 3: The Communication and Navigation Radios

☑ Use your finger to turn the inner or outer rings of the **COM/VLOC Tuning Knob**, located in the lower left corner of the IFD. These control the numbers of the selected frequency box. The outer (larger) ring controls "ones" and "tens" digits of the frequency; the inner (smaller) ring controls the "tenths" and "hundredths" digits. Keep adjusting the knobs until you tune the Melbourne ground frequency, 121.90.

Figure 3 - 3 Changing a Communications Frequency

☑ Press the **Frequency Swap Key**. This will exchange the active and standby communications frequencies, enabling you to transmit on the Melbourne ground control frequency.

Figure 3 - 4 The Frequency Swap Key

Lesson 3: The Communication and Navigation Radios

Note that the words **Melbourne Gnd** are displayed underneath the frequency 121.9 in the active communications frequency box. The IFD540 knows your current position and it knows the communications frequencies around you, so it automatically displays the name of the facility you are talking to. This is a big help when you want to make sure your radio is tuned correctly.

After the ground frequency has been tuned you can contact ground control and get your taxi clearance. When you reach the end of the runway it's time to call the tower on 118.2. You could enter the tower frequency by using the COM/VLOC tuning knob, as you did with ground control. But let's try a different method which uses the IFD540's touch screen.

☑   Instead of turning either of the tuning rings, tap in the middle of either the active or standby communications box (either of the two on top). This will bring up a **Frequency Tuning Keyboard** on the touch screen.

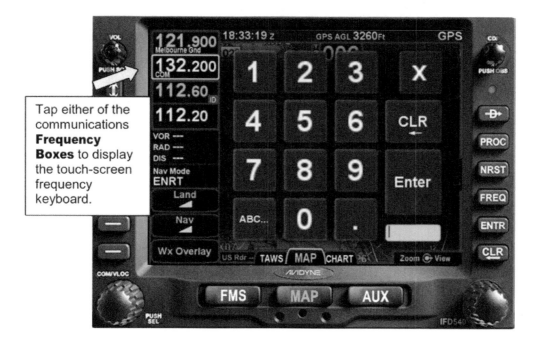

Figure 3 - 5 Bringing Up the On-Screen Keyboard

☑   Tap on the keyboard numbers to enter the tower frequency numbers **1, 8,** and **2**. The IFD already knows you are tuning in the 100 mHz band, so typing all three numbers before the decimal are unnecessary. Tap on the on-screen **Enter Button** when you have finished. You could also press the **ENTR** key on the right side of the display, or press the lower right knob.

Note that you do not have to enter the first 1, the decimal point, or the last 0. The IFD540 puts those in for you.

Figure 3 - 6 Tuning with the On-Screen Keyboard

☑ When you have keyed in the tower frequency, press the **Frequency Swap Key** on the left side of the display to exchange the active and standby communications frequency.

Note: No matter how you enter a new frequency (knob or touch screen), the frequency is always placed in the standby frequency box. It never becomes active until you press the frequency swap key.

Figure 3 - 7 The Frequency Swap Key

Lesson 3: The Communication and Navigation Radios

You are now ready to talk to the tower. Note that **Melbourne Twr** is displayed in the top box, confirming that you are talking to the right ATC facility.

Tuning the VHF Navigation Radio

Before you take off it would be a good idea to tune the navigation radio so you can head for your initial fix without confusion. Remember that the route of flight was planned over the Ormond Beach and St. Augustine VORs. Let's get those tuned in.

If you look at any of the pictures above you will see that there is a cyan box surrounding the second (standby) frequency window. The cyan box means that this is the selected frequency window; it's the one that is going to be tuned. Since the top two frequency windows are for communications, all your tuning so far has been for the communications radio. But now you must tune the navigation radio.

Try this:

☑ Press the **COM/VLOC Tuning Knob** in the lower left corner of the IFD. Pressing this knob causes the **Selected Frequency Box** to alternate between the communications and navigation radios. In this case, pressing it once will cause the navigation radio standby frequency to become selected, so it can now be tuned. You can confirm this by observing that it is surrounded by a cyan box.

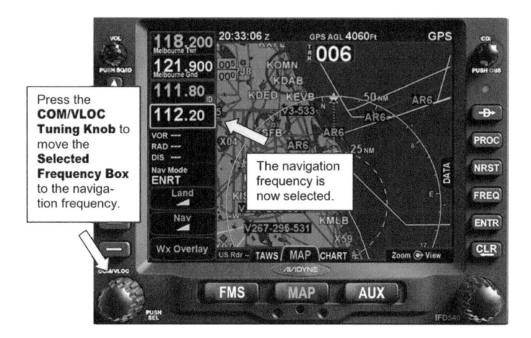

Figure 3 - 8 Selecting a Nav Frequency Box

☑ If you don't do anything for 20 seconds the selected frequency box will revert back to the communications radio, where it normally stays.

☑ While the cyan selected frequency box is still around the standby navigation frequency window, use the **COM/VLOC Tuning Knob** to tune in your new VOR frequency, 112.6. Or, you can tap either of the two navigation frequencies and use the on-screen keyboard.

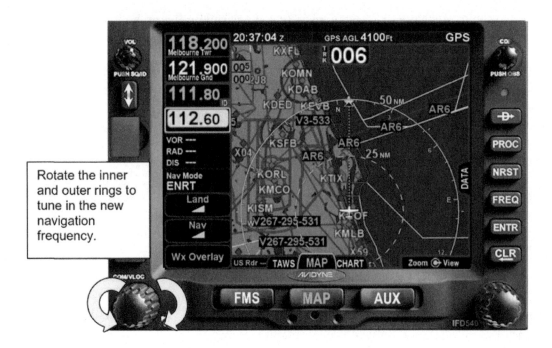

Rotate the inner and outer rings to tune in the new navigation frequency.

Figure 3 - 9 Tuning a Nav Frequency

☑ When the new frequency has been entered, and while the cyan box still surrounds the standby navigation frequency window, press the **Frequency Swap Key** to exchange the active and standby navigation frequencies. Your navigation radio is now tuned to the first VOR on your route.

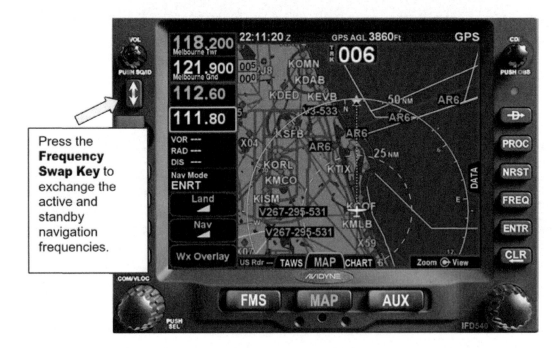

Press the **Frequency Swap Key** to exchange the active and standby navigation frequencies.

Figure 3 - 10 The Frequency Swap Key

Use the same procedure to enter the St. Augustine VOR frequency, 109.4, into the navigation standby frequency box. Having this set up before takeoff will lower your enroute work load.

Lesson 3: The Communication and Navigation Radios

The next VOR frequency has been entered into the standby navigation frequency box.

Figure 3 - 11 Setting the Standby Nav Frequency

Putting the IFD540 into VLOC Mode

There is one last thing you must do before takeoff. The IFD540 is a GPS navigator. It normally wants to fly preset flight plans using GPS navigation. But you haven't learned about GPS yet; you just want to use the VOR navigation that you've used before. How can you do that?

The navigation source of the IFD540 is controlled by the **CDI Knob**, located in its upper right corner. Immediately above and left of the CDI knob the letters **GPS** are shown on your screen. This indicates that you are in GPS navigation mode. The letters are yellow because you have not set up a flight plan yet. You must tell the IFD540 that you want to use your VOR for navigation.

Proceed as follows:

☑ Rotate the **CDI Knob** to the right or left. When you do so, the letters **VLOC** will appear where **GPS** used to be.

VLOC stands for **VOR/Localizer**. When the IFD540 is in VLOC mode it is using VHF-based VOR or localizer signals for navigation, and the information from those signals is being fed to the navigation indicator installed in your aircraft. You can use the CDI knob on your nav indicator to set a course and follow it, just like you have always done. The IFD540 still knows its position from the GPS signal, and will still plot your airplane on the moving map. But your navigation indicator is driven by the VOR/localizer signal.

> **Note:** The letters **VLOC** are displayed in yellow because you are not receiving a valid VOR signal yet. They will turn green when the VOR is picked up.

> **Note:** The IFD540 simulator does not simulate VORs very well. In fact, it NEVER receives them, so the VLOC signal never turns green in the simulator. The real IFD unit in your aircraft behaves differently.

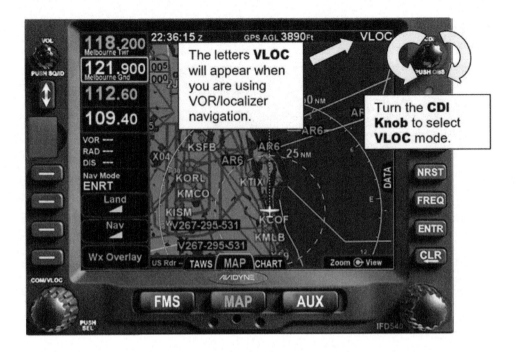

Figure 3 - 12 Changing to VLOC Navigation

Controlling the Volume

You now have your radios all tuned and you are ready for takeoff. There's one last thing – you should probably be ready to turn up the volume on your communications radio, just in case the engine noise is too loud to hear the tower.

Try this:

☑ Turn the **VOL/SQ/ID Knob**, located in the upper left corner of the IFD540. As you turn the knob the radio's volume will go up and down. Also, a green **Volume Bar** will appear underneath the frequency of the radio that is being controlled. The volume bar will grow bigger or smaller to indicate the loudness of your radio.

When you turn the volume knob, you are controlling the volume of the communications (the top) radio. This is the default selection. If you want to change the volume of the navigation radio, simply select it by pressing the **COM/VLOC Tuning Knob**. This will make the cyan selection box jump to the navigation frequency box, and you can change that radio's volume. Remember that the selection box will automatically jump back to the communications radio after 20 seconds of inactivity.

Note: It is often very useful to turn off the radio's squelch circuit before you adjust the volume so you can hear the effects of your changes. You can do this by momentarily pressing the **VOL/SQ/ID Knob**. One press turns the squelch off, another turns it on again.

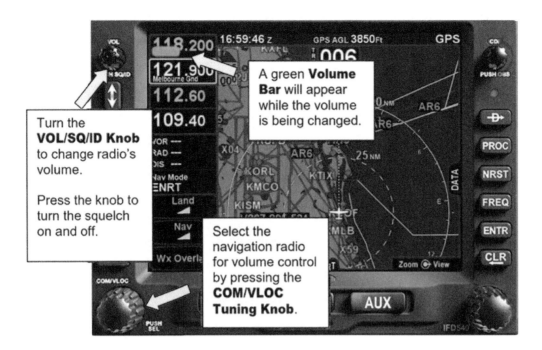

Figure 3 - 13 Controlling Volume and Squelch

Checking the VOR Identification Code

Your first navigation fix after takeoff is the Ormond Beach VOR on frequency 112.6. You have verified that you tuned the correct frequency, but it's always a good idea to check the ID signal of the VOR just to make sure it's not out of service. How can you do this?

The easiest way to check the ID of a navigational facility is to just let the IFD do the work for you. It will automatically "listen" to the identification Morse code signal, decode it, and display it for you. The station ID, radial, and distance will be displayed under the radio frequency boxes, as shown below.

Note: The display shown is in the default configuration. The information displayed below the frequency boxes can be changed by the user. Your IFD may be set up differently.

Note: The distance from the navigational facility looks like a DME distance, but it's not. The IFD does not include a DME receiver. The distance displayed is a GPS distance, not a DME distance. There can be slight differences between the two, because DME is "slant range" distance, while GPS is not. For example, if you are directly over a station at 10,000 feet, a DME receiver will show that you are two miles away, while GPS will show a distance of zero.

Note: The IFD540 and IFD440 simulators to do not simulate VOR stations. Therefore, they do not show the VOR identification, radial, and distance as the real IFDs do.

You can also check the identification signal the old-fashioned way, by listening to the Morse code ID. Use the following procedure. (This for a real airplane; the simulator does not simulate nav ID signals.):

☑ Select the NAV input on your audio panel so you can hear the output of the IFD navigation radio.

☑ Press the **COM/VLOC Tuning Knob** once. This will select the navigation radio frequency box.

☑ Press the **VOL/SQ/ID Knob.** This turns off the radio's ID filter, so you can hear the identification signal more clearly. The letters **ID** will be displayed in blue.

☑ Turn the **VOL/SQ/ID Knob** to adjust the volume of the navigation radio audio signal.

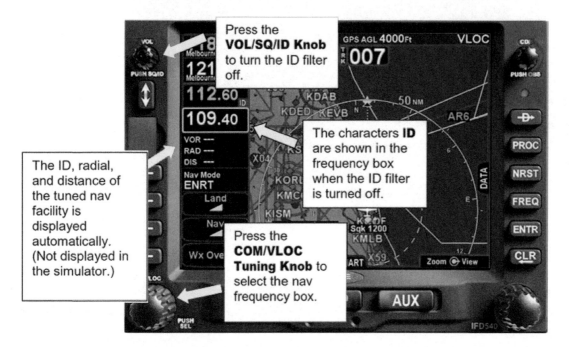

Figure 3 - 14 Checking the Nav Facility ID

Quick-Tuning to the Emergency Frequency

The IFD offers a fast and easy way to tune to the emergency frequency, 121.5. This could be very useful if you encountered an in-flight problem, such as an engine failure, that required fast action.

Use this procedure:

☑ Push and hold the Frequency Swap key for about three seconds, until 121.5 appears in the active frequency window.

The 121.5 emergency frequency is now tuned and ready for use.

Press and hold the **Frequency Swap** key to quickly tune the 121.5 emergency frequency.

Figure 3 - 15 Quick-Tuning the 121.5 Emergency Frequency

IFD440 Differences

The navigation and communications radios on the IFD440 are controlled in exactly the same way as they are on the IFD540. There are only a few differences in the way that the information is displayed:

- The IFD440's display doesn't have room for four frequency boxes. Therefore, only the selected frequency boxes are displayed. Normally, this will be the communications frequencies. Press the COM/VLOC Tuning Knob to select and display the navigation frequencies.

- The Frequency Swap Button on the IFD440 is oriented horizontally instead of vertically as it is on the IFD540.

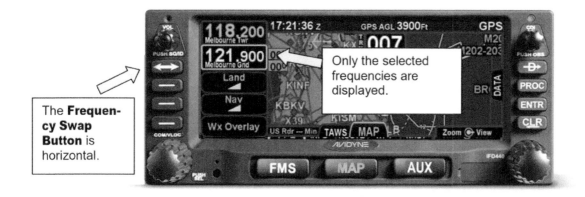

Only the selected frequencies are displayed.

The **Frequency Swap Button** is horizontal.

Figure 3 - 16 IFD440 Frequency Display

Lesson 3: The Communication and Navigation Radios

IFD545, IFD510, and IFD410 Differences

The IFD545, IFD510, and IFD410 do not have VHF navigation or communication capability. This lesson does not apply to them.

Lesson Review

In this lesson you learned the basics of how to communicate and perform basic VOR navigation with your new IFD540 or IFD440. The items that were covered are:

Tuning the Communication and Navigation Radios

- There are four Frequency Boxes located in the upper left corner of the IFD5XX's display.

- The top two Frequency Boxes are for the communications radio; the bottom two are for the navigation radio.

- In each case, the top frequency is the active frequency. The bottom is the standby frequency.

- The frequency surrounded by a cyan box is the selected frequency. Only standby frequencies can be selected and edited directly.

- You can make either the communications or navigation frequency the selected frequency by pressing the COM/VLOC tuning knob, located in the lower left corner of the IFD.

- The selected frequency is tuned by rotating the inner and outer rings of the COM/VLOC tuning knob. You can also enter frequencies by using the pop-up keyboard on the touch-screen.

- The active and standby frequencies are exchanged by pressing the Frequency Swap key, located left of the display. This allows you to transmit or receive on a new frequency.

Using VLOC Mode for VHF Navigation

- You can see what mode the IFD is in by looking at the GPS/VLOC indicator, located in the unit's upper right corner.

- In order to navigate using a VOR or a localizer, you must switch the IFD from GPS mode to VLOC mode.

- Changing between GPS and VLOC modes is controlled by rotating the CDI Knob, located in the upper right corner of the IFD.

- When the IFD goes into VLOC mode it still tracks its map position from GPS signals, but the navigation indicator in your aircraft displays information from the VOR or localizer that you tuned.

Controlling the Audio Volume

- The volume of your receiver is controlled by turning the VOL/SQ/ID Knob, located in the upper left corner of the IFD.

- Only the volume of the selected radio is changed. You can select the other one by pressing the COM/VLOC tuning knob.

Lesson 3: The Communication and Navigation Radios

- The changing volume is displayed by a green Volume Bar in the active frequency box of the selected radio. The bar only appears while the volume is being changed.

- You can turn the squelch of the selected radio on and off by pressing the VOL/SQ/ID knob.

Checking the Navigation Facility ID Signal

- The IFD will automatically decode and display the identification signal of the navigational facility that is tuned. The display of this information is shown under the navigation frequency boxes. This is the default configuration; it can be changed by the user.

- The IFD also displays the distance from the navigational facility. This is a GPS distance, not a DME distance.

- To listen to the Morse ID signal manually you must first turn off the IFD's ID filter. This is done by selecting the nav frequency box by pressing the COM/VLOC tuning knob, then pressing the VOL/SQ/ID Knob. The letters ID will be displayed in blue when the ID filter is turned off.

- The IFD5XX/4XX simulators do not include a simulation of VOR stations.

Quick-Tuning to the Emergency Frequency

- Press and hold the Frequency Swap key for three seconds to quick-tune to the 121.5 emergency frequency.

Lesson 4: Building and Flying a Simple Flight Plan

Most of your work with the IFDs will involve building and flying flight plans. It pays to make sure that you understand them thoroughly. This course will use two lessons to fully explore flight plans: This lesson will introduce flight plans and let you build and fly a simple one; the next one will add more complex techniques.

In this lesson you will learn to program simple clearances on the active flight plan page. You will learn how to follow your flight on the moving map. At the end of the lesson you will be familiar with easy flight plans and ready to proceed to more complex ones.

Flight Plan Concepts

Waypoints

Waypoints are the fundamental building blocks of any flight plan. A waypoint is simply a position defined in space. Each waypoint has a name and a location, defined by its latitude/longitude coordinates. The internal database of each IFD contains thousands of waypoints, determined by the geographical coverage area that you have purchased for your unit.

Common types of waypoints are navigational aids such as VORs and NDBs, airports, and the named intersections on navigational charts. You can also create and store up to 500 of your own waypoints.

Flight Plans

A flight plan is simply a series of waypoints in a specified sequence. It can also include holding patterns, procedure turns, and instrument approaches. Flight plans are displayed on the FMS FPL page. The example in the figure below shows a simple flight plan as it appears on an IFD. The flight plan starts at the Chicago Executive airport (KPWK), flies over two waypoints (BAE and OSH), and ends at the Oshkosh (KOSH) airport.

Look at the color coding of the waypoints:

- Origin and destination airports are shown in blue.

- The next waypoint, which you are flying to now, is shown in magenta.

- Other waypoints are shown in gray.

> **Note:** The first waypoint in a flight plan is usually the origin. An origin must be an airport; it cannot be any other kind of waypoint. Flights that begin at locations other than database airports do not have an origin; they simply have a first waypoint along the route.

> **Note:** A flight plan can have more than one destination airport. Each one can have an arrival procedure and an instrument approach associated with it. This is useful if you would like to pre-program your alternate airport before takeoff.

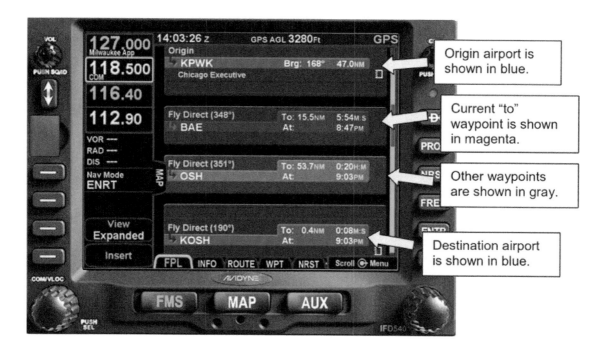

Figure 4 - 1 Elements of a Flight Plan

Here is the same flight plan, as shown on the MAP page while it is being flown. Your aircraft is shown superimposed on the flight plan leg in its current position. The "current" leg of the flight is the leg that goes to the next waypoint. It is shown in magenta. The "next" leg is the leg after the next waypoint. It is displayed with a magenta barber pole. When you look at the map display you can easily see what leg you are navigating on now and, equally important, what your aircraft will do when it crosses the next waypoint.

Figure 4 - 2 Flight Plan Legs

Lesson 4: Building and Flying a Simple Flight Plan

The Scenario

You will learn how to build flight plans by working with a simple scenario.

To begin this exercise, imagine that you are at your home airport at Chicago Executive (KPWK). You are preparing for your annual trip to EAA AirVenture at Oshkosh (KOSH). You receive the following clearance from Chicago Executive Clearance Delivery:

> **"Cessna 1291S, you are cleared from the Chicago Executive airport to the Oshkosh airport via the Badger VOR, climb and maintain 4000, squawk 1234."**

Let's get ready to fly this trip.

Building a Simple Flight Plan

Start the IFD540 Simulator and Display the FPL Page

Flight plans are always built on the FMS FPL page. You can display this page by pressing the FMS rocker under the display, then selecting the FPL tab.

- Start the IFD540 simulator program on your iPad.

- Press the **FMS** rocker. This will display one of the FMS pages. (It may be displayed already when you start the simulator.)

- Press on the left side of the **FMS** rocker. This will sequentially select the tabs at the bottom of the FMS pages. Stop when you have selected the **FPL** tab. Or, you can select the **FPL** tab directly by simply tapping it on the touch screen.

- If an origin waypoint is already displayed, press the **CLR** key to delete it.

The display should look like this:

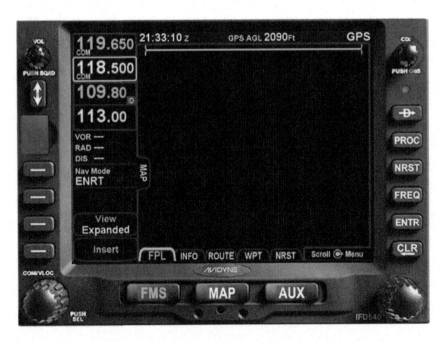

Figure 4 - 3 An Empty Flight Plan

Lesson 4: Building and Flying a Simple Flight Plan

Set the Origin Airport

When you power up an actual IFD5XX/4XX in your aircraft it will normally know its current position and will automatically set the first waypoint of the flight plan to that point. However, the simulator isn't as smart as the real IFD, so you will have to set your flight plan origin manually.

Notice the thin horizontal cyan line at the top of the display screen. This is the cursor. It has two modes; it can be an insert cursor (when it is between flight plan elements) or it can be an edit cursor (when it is around flight plan elements). Right now it is an insert cursor. It is the place in the flight plan where a new waypoint is going to be inserted. Since our flight plan is currently empty, the insert cursor is all by itself on the page.

The origin of your flight is the Chicago Executive airport, KPWK. To set the origin you will insert the new waypoint KPWK at the beginning of the flight plan.

☑ Press the **ENTR key**. An **Origin/Waypoint** selection box will appear.

☑ Press the **ENTR** key again to select **Origin**.

Figure 4 - 4 Flight Plan Origin

☑ Turn the inner and outer rings of the **IFD Multi-Function** knob to enter the characters **K, P, W**, and **K**. Turn the inner (smaller) knob to change individual characters. Turn the outer knob to move between the character positions you want to change with the inner knob.

> **Note:** An actual IFD will know its position when it was last turned off. It will automatically display that same position as an origin when it is turned back on. If necessary, the origin position can be deleted by pressing the **CLR** key.

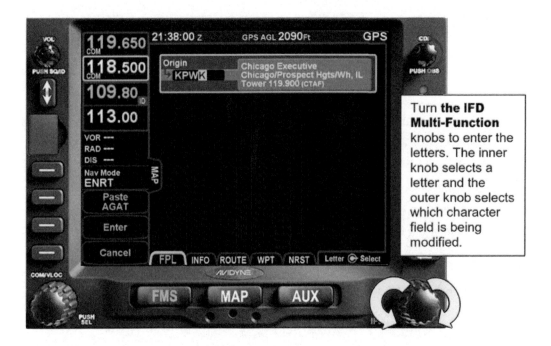

Figure 4 - 5 Entering the Origin Waypoint ID

☑ When you have finished entering all four characters, press the **ENTR** key to accept the new origin and insert it into your flight plan.

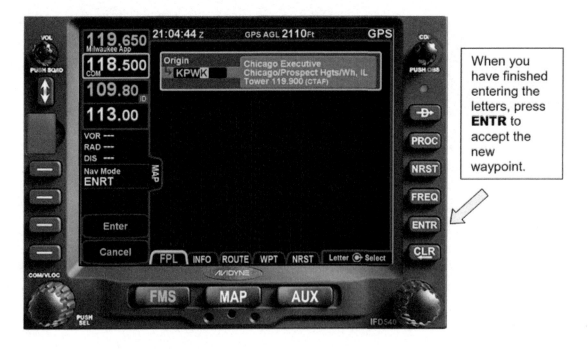

Figure 4 - 6 Press ENTR to Accept the Origin

☑ The new origin has now been entered into your flight plan. It is an airport, so it is displayed in blue. The cyan **Insert Cursor** is positioned immediately under it, ready to insert another waypoint.

Note: Remember that only airports can be origins. Initial waypoints that aren't airports are just entered as the first fix in the flight plan.

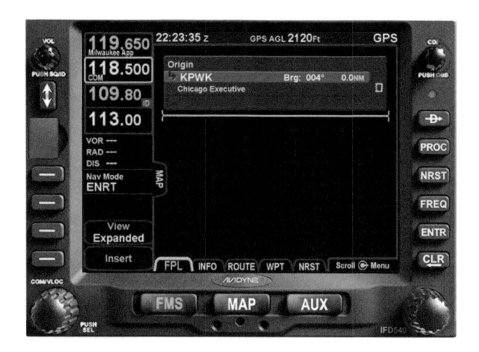

Figure 4 - 7 Completed Origin Entry

Enter More Waypoints

Now that your departure airport has been set up, you can enter the rest of the waypoints in the flight plan.

Your clearance was from the Chicago Executive Airport to the Badger VOR, to the Oshkosh Airport. The identifiers for the Badger and Oshkosh waypoints are BAE, and KOSH.

Add those waypoints to your flight plan as follows:

☑ Check that the screen looks like the figure above, with the **Insert Cursor** positioned under the **KPWK** waypoint. If it isn't, rotate the **IFD Multi-Function** knob until it is.

☑ Press the **ENTR** key. This will bring up a **Waypoint** dialog box.

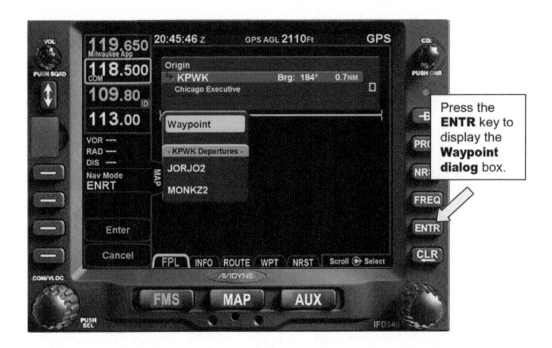

Figure 4 - 8 Waypoint Entry Dialog Box

☑ Press the **ENTR** key again. This accepts the **Waypoint** option, which tells the IFD that you want to enter a new waypoint.

☑ The IFD will automatically display a suggested waypoint that is near your current location. You might see a different one than OBK, which is shown below. In any case, it's not likely to be BAE, which is the waypoint you want.

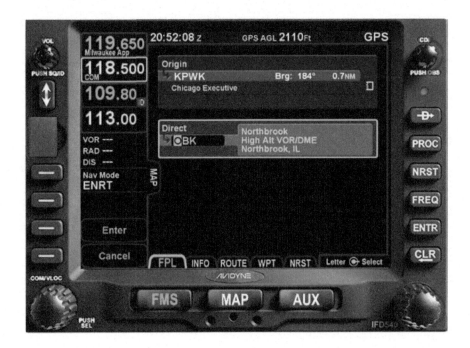

Figure 4 - 9 Waypoint Entry Field

☑ Enter the letters for the **BAE** waypoint with the **IFD Multi-Function** knob, as you did with the origin waypoint. Or, you can use the IFD's touch screen capabilities.

☑ To use the on-screen keyboard, simply tap in the middle of the name of the waypoint shown on your screen. (Tap the middle of OBK in the example above.) The keyboard will appear.

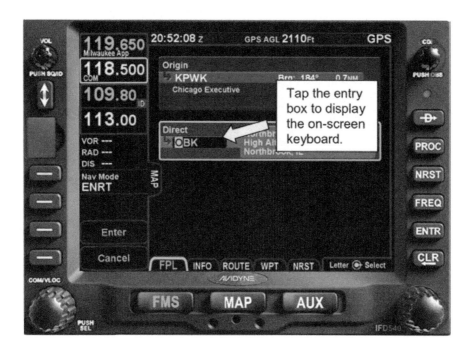

Figure 4 - 10 Using the On Screen Keyboard to Enter a Waypoint

☑ When the on-screen keyboard appears, simply tap on the letters **B**, **A**, and **E**, to spell the identifier that you want. Tap the on-screen keyboard's **Enter** button or press the **ENTR Key** when the identifier is complete.

Note: You can also press the physical **ENTR** key on the right side of the IFD or the center of the IFD Multi-Function knob. Each performs the same function as the screen's **Enter** button.

Lesson 4: Building and Flying a Simple Flight Plan

*Figure 4 - 11 Using the On Screen Keyboard to Enter a Waypoint

After you press **Enter**, the new waypoint is accepted into the flight plan.

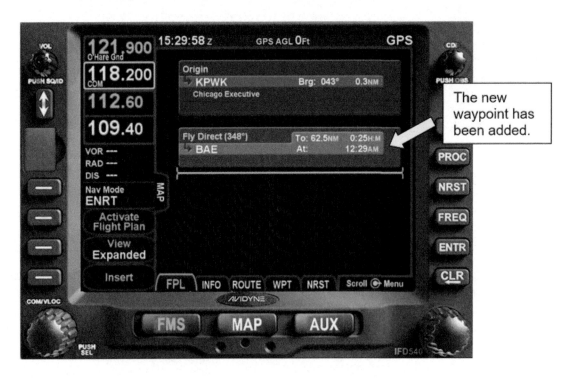

Figure 4 - 12 Flight Plan After Waypoint Entry

Your new flight plan now has two waypoints: the origin airport and the first en-route waypoint. Your clearance was KPWK-BAE-KOSH. That means that you have one more waypoint to go: the Oshkosh airport. You can add it in the same way that you entered the BAE waypoint:

☑ Turn the **IFD Multi-Function** knob until the insertion cursor appears under the last waypoint, **BAE**. (You can also tap the screen under the last waypoint.)

☑ Press the **ENTR** key to bring up the Waypoint dialog box.

☑ Press the **ENTR** key again to accept the fact that you want to enter a waypoint and bring up the waypoint ID entry dialog box.

☑ When the waypoint box appears, use the on-screen keyboard or the **IFD Multi-Function** knob to enter **K, O, S,** and **H**, the ID of the last waypoint in the flight plan.

☑ Press the on-screen **Enter** button or the **ENTR** key to accept the new waypoint.

☑ Press the **Activate Flight Plan** line select key on the left side of the screen.

☑ The completed and activated flight plan will look like the following figure. The active waypoint (BAE) has changed from gray to magenta, the yellow GPS navigation mode indication has changed to green, and the last waypoint is displayed in blue since it's an airport.

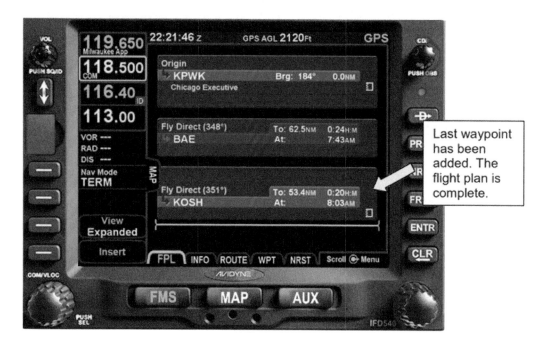

Figure 4 - 13 Completed Flight Plan

Your first flight plan is now complete!

Note on Entering Flight Plans: Remember that pressing the center of the IFD Multi-Function knob is equivalent to pressing the **ENTR** key. That means that you can program most flight plans without ever taking your hand off the knob. Use the "twist and push" method to move the cursor and enter letters with the inner and outer knobs, then press the center of the knob to accept the entry.

Note on Activating Flight Plans: In the actual aircraft a flight plan must be activated before it is used. This is done by pressing the Activate line select key. If you do not activate a flight plan it will activate itself automatically when the IFD senses that you have taken off.

Lesson 4: Building and Flying a Simple Flight Plan

Flying a Flight Plan

Now that you have entered your first flight plan into the IFD, you can use the simulator to fly it and see how you can use the IFD to monitor your trip.

Display the MAP Page

The MAP page is the IFD's most useful tool for keeping track of your flight. The first thing you'll do is display it on your screen.

Do the following:

☑ Press the **MAP** rocker under the display screen. This is one of the three **Page Function** rockers. They are used to select which page is displayed on the display screen.

Figure 4 - 14 Displaying the MAP Page

☑ There are three pages under the **MAP** rocker: the **MAP** page, the **CHART** page, and the **TAWS** page. They are shown by the three tabs at the bottom of the display screen. You can select any one of them by pressing on the right or left side of the **MAP** rocker to cycle from one tab to the next, or by touching the desired tab directly on the touch screen. (Chart tab not available on IFD4XX versions).

For now, you want to use the **MAP** page, so make sure that the **MAP** tab is selected.

The page might not look like the one shown below. The airplane will not be in the same location, and the map may not be in track-up orientation. (Track up is discussed in the paragraphs below.)

Figure 4 - 15 Using the MAP Rocker

Basic Map Features

The upper right corner of the map should display the characters **GPS** in green. This indicates that the IFD is navigating on a current flight plan leg. The GPS caption will be displayed in yellow if there is no flight plan, if the flight plan has not been activated, if there is no active flight plan leg, or if no GPS signal is being received.

Your aircraft's current position and the flight plan leg it is on is shown in the middle of the map. The current leg is displayed as a magenta line, while the next leg is shown with a magenta barber pole. Legs behind you are displayed in white. All legs beyond the next leg are also displayed in white.

> **Note:** It is very important to always be aware of which leg is displayed in magenta. *The magenta leg is always the current leg.* It's the leg that the IFD is trying to fly, and the one that you will go to if the autopilot is engaged and coupled to the IFD.

The airplane symbol is surrounded by two range rings which give you an idea of the scale of the map. Each range ring has a mileage number displayed on its upper right side.

Your current ground track is shown at the top of the map. (This number could also be your heading if your IFD is connected to an external compass system.)

Figure 4 - 16 MAP Page Fundamentals

North Up and Track Up

When the map is oriented "north up," the top of the map is its northern edge. When the map is oriented "track up," your aircraft's current ground track is at the top of the map.

Displaying the map north up or track up is a matter of personal preference. Often it is easier to maintain your situational awareness if you are in track up mode.

> Note: If your IFD is connected to a heading source such as an EFIS display, the map will default to heading Up mode instead of track up mode. This can be changed on the **User Options** screen. Refer to the **User Options Tab** section in Lesson 11.

To switch between north up and track up modes, do the following:

☑ While the **MAP** page is displayed, switch between north up and track up by pressing on the **IFD Multi-Function** knob. Each time you press the map will sequence to one of three possible orientations:

1. North up with your aircraft at the center of the screen.

2. Track up with your aircraft at the bottom part of the screen (called "240° arc view").

3. Track up with your aircraft at the center of the screen (called "360° view").

☑ You can tell if you are in track up, north up, or heading up mode by looking at the labels at the top of the display:

- If you are in north up mode a **North** symbol is shown in the upper right corner.

- If you are in track up mode the **North** symbol will not be displayed and the letters **TRK** appear to the left of the track box.

- If you are in heading up mode neither the **North** symbol nor the **TRK** letters are displayed.

Figure 4 - 17 Track Up Mode

Figure 4 - 18 North Up Mode

Zooming, Panning, and Centering the Map

You can display the map at different scales and look at different parts of it by zooming, panning, and re-centering it. Try this:

☑ Zoom the map by rotating the **IFD Multi-Function** knob. Rotating right zooms in; rotating left zooms out. Note that the mileage numbers on the range rings change as you zoom in and out.

Lesson 4: Building and Flying a Simple Flight Plan

You can also zoom the map by "pinching" it with your fingers on the touch screen display.

Figure 4 - 19 Zooming the Map In and Out

☑ Pan the map by placing your finger anywhere on the display and "dragging" it across the screen. There is no way to pan the map without using the touch screen.

Figure 4 - 20 Panning the Map

☑ The map will automatically re-center itself after 20 seconds. You can manually re-center it by pressing the **IFD Multi-Function** knob or by double-tapping anywhere on the map.

Figure 4 - 21 Re-Centering the Map

Controlling the Detail Displayed on the Map

When the MAP page is being displayed you can control the amount of detail that is displayed by "decluttering" it. This is accomplished by pushing the two line select keys on the left side of the map.

The two "declutter" line select keys control the amount of detail shown. Each press of a key reduces the number of elements that are displayed. The amount of decluttering that is in effect is indicated by the amount of cyan fill in the small triangle on the right side of the button.

The top declutter key (the second line select key) controls the amount of geographical detail that is shown. The bottom declutter key (immediately underneath) controls navigational detail.

Do the following:

☑ Press the top **Declutter** line select key. Each time you press it the amount of geographic detail is reduced and the amount of fill in the top triangle gets smaller.

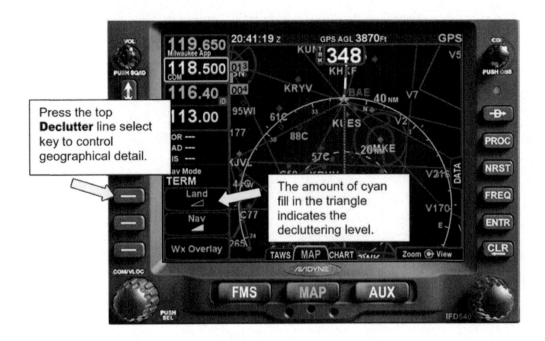

Figure 4 - 22 The Land De-Cluttering Key

☑ Press the bottom **Declutter** line select key. Each time you press it the amount of navigational detail is reduced and the amount of fill in the bottom triangle gets smaller.

Figure 4 - 23 The Nav De-Cluttering Key

☑ The map is almost completely clear when both decluttering keys are at their minimum level. Only the airplane, the flight plan, and the range rings are displayed. Since display of traffic targets do not declutter, this setting essentially provides a **dedicated traffic page**.

Note: You can control exactly which geographic and navigation features are shown at each level of decluttering by using the **SETUP** tab of the **AUX** page. This will be explained in a later lesson.

Setting both decluttering keys to their minimum levels almost clears the map.

Figure 4 - 24 Maximum De-Cluttering

Showing the Datablocks

You can display a large amount of very useful information about your flight by using Datablocks. These blocks appear on the left, top, and right side of the map.

For example, some of the information you can put in the datablocks is:

- Your current ground speed.

- The location of the nearest airport.

- The distances to the next waypoint and your final destination.

- The amount of time you have been airborne.

- Your fuel on board and how much fuel you will have at your destination (if your IFD receives fuel quantity information from an external fuel computer).

You have complete control over what information is displayed in all the datablocks. This is done by using the Datablock Setup line select key on the SETUP tab of the AUX pages. This will be discussed in a later lesson.

The datablocks on the left and top sides of the map are shown at all times. You can control whether the right datablocks are displayed or not.

Do the following:

☑ Tap on the **Data** side tab on the right side of the screen.

Lesson 4: Building and Flying a Simple Flight Plan

F.igure 4 - 25 Displaying the Datablocks

☑ When you press the **DATA** side tab, the right datablocks are displayed.

☑ You can also Press and hold either side of the MAP button to show/hide the right datablocks.

Figure 4 - 26 Right Datablocks

☑ The IFD5XX/4XX will allow you to place more datablocks on the right side than can be visible all at once. You can scroll them up and down by placing your finger on one of them and dragging it up or down.

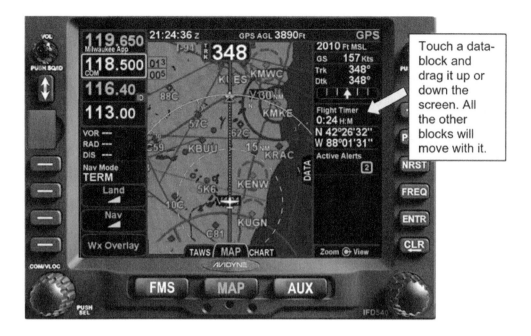

Figure 4 - 27 Scrolling the Right Datablocks

☑   Tap or click the **DATA** side tab again and the right datablocks will disappear.

Figure 4 - 28 Removing the Right Datablocks

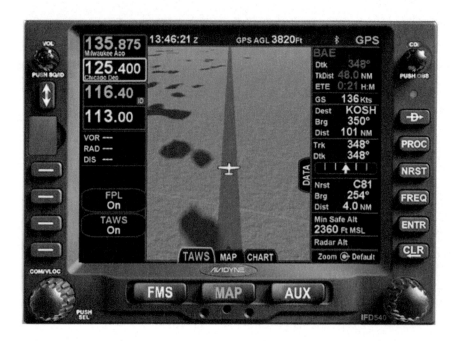

Figure 4 - 29 TAWS tab - Datablocks on

☑ Press the left side of the **MAP** rocker or tap the **TAWS** tab to view the exocentric 3D Synthetic Vision view. Use the **DATA** side tab to display or remove the right datablocks.

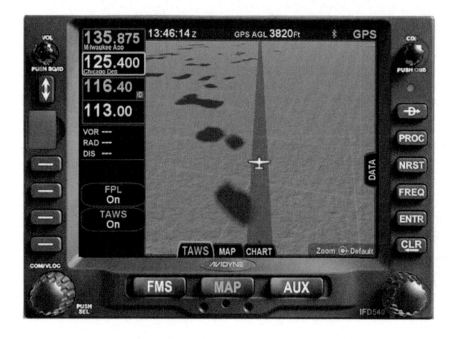

Figure 4 - 30   TAWS tab - Datablocks off

Use the IFD to Monitor Your Progress

As your simulated flight continues the IFD keeps track of your position and updates the information in the datablocks. When you reach BAE, your first waypoint, your aircraft will automatically make the turn and head for the next waypoint. (Your real airplane will do the same thing if it is connected to an autopilot that is compatible with GPS steering.)

Three more things happen when you cross a waypoint:

1. The next flight plan leg turns magenta to indicate that it is now the current leg.

2. The leg after that turns into a barber pole to indicate that it is now the next leg.

3. Your old leg turns white to indicate that it is now behind you.

This will continue until you reach your final destination.

IFD440 and IFD410 Differences

The flight plan page and the map page of the IFD440/410 work exactly the same as their counterparts on the IFD5XX. The only difference is that the display screen of the IFD4XX is much smaller. That means that the map will show a much smaller area, and fewer fields are displayed in the right datablocks.

Also, the flight plan page only has room for a couple of waypoints to be visible. You may have to use your finger to scroll the touch screen up and down to see the insertion cursor. You can also use the IFD Multi-Function knob to move the cursor up and down. There is a 'Mini Flight Plan Format' setting, discussed in Chapter 11, that will switch the display to compact vertical waypoint size so you can view more waypoints per screen.

Figure 4 - 31 Flight Plan on IFD440

Lesson Review

We have covered a lot of material in this lesson. Let's review the major points:

Building Flight Plans

*   You will spend most of your time with the IFD5XX/4XX flying flight plans.

*   Each flight plan is simply an ordered sequence of waypoints, starting with an origin and proceeding to a destination.

Lesson 4: Building and Flying a Simple Flight Plan

- A waypoint is a named point in space. Common waypoints are VORs, NDBs, and airway intersections. You can also create your own "user" waypoints.

- Flight plans are built on the FPL tab of the FMS page.

- A flight plan is normally built by starting with the origin airport, adding intermediate waypoints, and finishing with the destination waypoint.

- Each waypoint is entered at the insertion cursor.

- The letters of the identifier for each waypoint can be entered by rotating the inner and outer knobs of the IFD Multi-Function knob, or by typing them on the touch screen display.

- The airports in your flight plan are displayed in blue, the next waypoint is magenta, and all other waypoints are gray.

- A flight plan must be activated before it can be used. It can be activated by pressing the Activate line select key, or it will activate automatically when the IFD senses that you have taken off.

- The caption **GPS** will appear in green in the upper right corner of the IFD when an active flight plan leg exists. It will be in yellow if there is no active flight plan leg or if no GPS signal is being received.

Using the MAP Page

- Your flight plan is also displayed on the MAP page. The legs are color-coded to show your progress:

    - The legs behind you are white

    - The current leg is magenta

    - The next leg is a magenta barber pole

    - All legs after the next leg are white

- The magenta leg is always the current leg. It's the one that the IFD is currently trying to fly. Your aircraft will automatically intercept and track this leg if the autopilot is coupled to the IFD.

- You can change between north up and heading or track up orientations by pressing the IFD Multi-Function knob.

- You can zoom the map in and out by rotating the IFD Multi-Function knob.

- You can pan the map by dragging your finger across the touch screen.

- You can recenter the map by waiting for 20 seconds or pressing the IFD Multi-Function knob or double-tapping anywhere on the map screen.

- You can display the right side datablocks by touching the DATA tab on the right side of the touch screen.

- As your flight progresses the IFD will follow each leg on the MAP page. Your airplane will track your flight plan too if your IFD is connected to a compatible autopilot.

Lesson 5: Changing a Flight Plan

The previous lesson showed you how to build and fly simple flight plans. If the world were simple, this might be all you need to know. Unfortunately, flying is never simple. Your routing often changes, so you need to know how to modify a flight plan to fly the new route.

In this lesson you will learn to make changes to an existing flight plan. Changes can be as simple as going directly to an existing waypoint, or as complicated as diverting to different destination.

At the end of this lesson you will be comfortable with creating and modifying simple waypoint-to-waypoint flight plans. You will be ready to move on to more complex flight plans which could include airways, departure and arrival procedures, and instrument approaches.

The Scenario

As we did in the previous lesson, you will learn how to build flight plans by working with a scenario. This one will be a little more complicated than the one you did previously.

To begin this exercise, imagine that you are at the St. Paul Downtown airport (KSTP). You are preparing for a trip to the Chicago Midway airport (KMDW). You receive the following clearance from Minneapolis Clearance Delivery:

> **"Cessna 1291S, you are cleared from the St. Paul Downtown airport to the Chicago Midway airport via the PRESS intersection, Nodine (ODI), Lone Rock (LNR), Madison (MSN), Northbrook (OBK), climb and maintain 5000, squawk 1234."**

Let's get ready to fly this trip.

Build the Flight Plan

Start the IFD540 Simulator and Display the FPL Page

Before you start your flight you will build the flight plan on the **FMS FPL** page.

- ☑ Start the IFD540 simulator program on your iPad.

- ☑ Press on the **FMS** rocker. This will display one of the **FMS** pages. (It may be displayed already when you start the simulator.)

- ☑ Press on the left side of the **FMS** rocker. This will sequentially select the tabs at the bottom of the **FMS** pages. Stop when you have selected the **FPL** tab.

Build the New Flight Plan

- ☑ Enter the new flight plan as you did in the previous exercise. The waypoints are **KSTP, PRESS, ODI, LNR, MSN, OBK, KMDW**.

- ☑ The entire flight plan will not fit on the IFD's display. You can scroll it up and down by dragging it with your finger, or you can turn the outer (larger) **IFD Multi-Function** knob. Either method will move the flight plan up or down the screen.

☑ New waypoints are always added at the position of the **Insertion Cursor**. When building a new flight plan, make sure that the cursor is always at the end of the waypoint list. Use the outer **IFD Multi-Function** knob to move it.

☑ If you make a mistake while you are entering a waypoint, press the **CLR** Key to stop entering that waypoint and start over again.

The completed flight plan is shown in the next two illustrations:

Figure 5 - 1 The Completed KSTP-KMDW Flight Plan

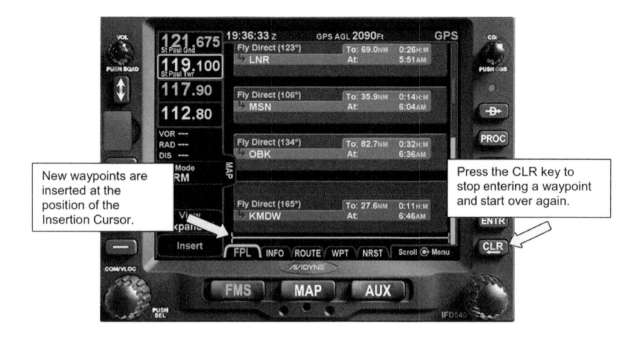

New waypoints are inserted at the position of the Insertion Cursor.

Press the CLR key to stop entering a waypoint and start over again.

Figure 5 - 2 The Completed KSTP-KMDW Flight Plan

Check the Flight Plan

Just typing in a new flight plan is not enough. A flight plan is not complete until you have checked it thoroughly. Many a pilot has wandered off course because he entered an incorrect route into the navigation system and then followed it blindly.

You must review each flight plan before using it!

After the flight plan has been entered, do the following:

☑ Use your cursor or the **IFD Multi-Function** knob to go back to the top of the flight plan.

☑ Scroll down through the flight plan and check each waypoint. Make sure that each is spelled correctly and that all are in the right order.

☑ Look at your flight plan on a map. You can see the flight plan and the map side-by-side if you tap on the **MAP Tab** on the left side of the flight plan page. A map window will open next to the flight plan waypoint list.

☑ Note: You can also press and hold either side of the FMS page button to do the same thing.

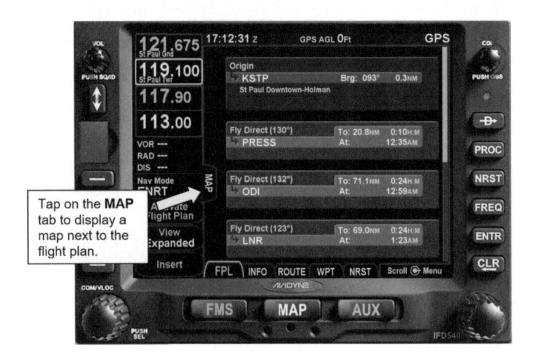

Figure 5 - 3 Opening the Flight Plan MAP Tab

☑ Press the line select key next to the **View Expanded** caption on the left side of the display screen. Keep clicking this key until the caption **View Cursor** appears. The words **Cursor Centered** will appear in the upper left corner of the map.

☑ Now you can turn the outer **IFD Multi-Function** knob to move up and down through your flight plan. As you do so, the map will re-center itself on the waypoint inside the **Cursor** box. By doing this you can move through the entire flight plan and review it both in text form and in graphic form on the map.

While reviewing the flight plan you should be especially alert for misspelled waypoints or waypoints that were entered in the wrong order. Both of these will be apparent by looking at the map.

Be sure to check the entire flight plan to make sure that your route makes sense.

Figure 5 - 4 Reviewing a Flight Plan with View Cursor

☑ Close the map by tapping on the FPL tab, or by pressing and holding either side of the FMS page button.

Figure 5 - 5 Closing the Flight Plan MAP Tab

☑ Activate the flight plan by pressing the **Activate Flight Plan** line select key. When you do so, note that:

• The **GPS** indicator in the upper right corner turns green.

• The first leg of the flight plan turns magenta.

Going Direct to a Waypoint on Your Flight Plan

The most common (and welcome) change to a flight plan is when you are cleared to fly directly to a waypoint that's already part of the planned route. Since the flight plan and its waypoints are already programmed into your navigator, it's easy to select any waypoint and go directly to it.

The Scenario

After you have built and checked your flight plan, you taxi out and take off.

The simulator is already set up from the previous paragraphs. The simulator started flying when you activated the flight plan. Now do the following:

☑ Press on the **MAP** page button under the display screen. This will display the moving map page so you can watch your flight.

☑ Let the airplane proceed until you are established on course to PRESS intersection. If necessary, press the **IFD Multi-Function** knob to put the map in track-up orientation.

Shortly after takeoff you receive the following clearance:

"Cessna 1291S, you are cleared direct to Madison."

The Madison VOR is already part of your planned route. Use the following procedure to go direct to a waypoint on your flight plan.

☑ Press on the **FMS** page button, followed by the **FPL** tab (if necessary) to display the flight plan page.

☑ If necessary, tap the **MAP** tab on the left side of the **FMS FPL** page to display a map next to the flight plan waypoints.

☑ Turn the outer **IFD Multi-Function** knob until the MSN waypoint is surrounded by a cyan box. The box is called the **Edit Cursor**. You can also select the MSN waypoint by simply tapping it on the touch screen.

Figure 5 - 6 Selecting the Direct-To Waypoint

☑ After MSN has been selected, press the **Direct-To** key on the right side of the display. (This is the key labeled by a **D** with an arrow through it.) As soon as you press this key a preview screen will appear.

The preview screen shows:

- A map showing your new route of flight, in cyan, superimposed on your old flight plan, in white.

- A green box showing the identity, bearing, and distance to your new "direct to" waypoint.

Figure 5 - 7 Previewing the Direct-To Waypoint

☑ You should check the **Direct-To** box and the map carefully to make sure that you will be going to the right place.

☑ When you are sure it's correct, press the **ENTR** key. Another green box will appear, asking you to confirm that you really want to go direct to MSN.

Figure 5 - 8 Activating the Direct-To Waypoint

☑ Make one last check and then press the **ENTR** key again. You are now proceeding directly to MSN, the selected waypoint.

Figure 5 - 9 Completed Direct-To

Note: Even after you go direct to one of the waypoints on your flight plan the "bypassed" waypoints are still available. You can always scroll backwards in the flight plan to see them, and you can still select any of them as a direct-to waypoint. This is often useful if a new routing doesn't quite go as expected and you want to return to your original route.

Lesson 5: Changing a Flight Plan

Going Direct to a Waypoint Not on Your Flight Plan

Unfortunately, things don't always work out as planned. Sometimes, due to weather, traffic, or the whims of ATC, you have to go direct to a waypoint that's not already on your flight plans. Let's see how to do this.

Continuing the previous scenario, you are now proceeding directly to MSN. But you soon get a new clearance:

> **"Cessna 1291S, previous traffic reports convective activity building between you and Madison. Turn left twenty degrees and proceed direct to the Volk VOR when able."**

The Volk VOR (VOK) is not part of your planned route. You could edit your flight plan to add it (which will be discussed later), or you could simply proceed directly to VOK and amend the flight plan when you've had time to figure out a new route. For this exercise, let's keep things simple and just go direct to VOK.

Proceed as follows:

☑ Press the **Direct-To** key, as you did before. The Direct-To box will appear, probably showing MSN as the direct-to waypoint. But it's irrelevant which waypoint appears in the box, since you're going to change it.

☑ Turn the **inner** (smaller) knob of the **IFD Multi-Function** knob. This will allow the waypoint identifier that appears in the direct-to box to be edited. Now use the inner and outer knobs to enter the letters **V, O,** and **K.** Remember, the inner knob selects individual letters, while the outer knob selects which letter position is being edited. Note that the IFD automatically inserts the names of nearby waypoints, so you don't have to enter the full identifier.

☑ You can also tap on the waypoint identifier in the direct-to box. An on-screen keyboard will appear and you can enter the letters directly.

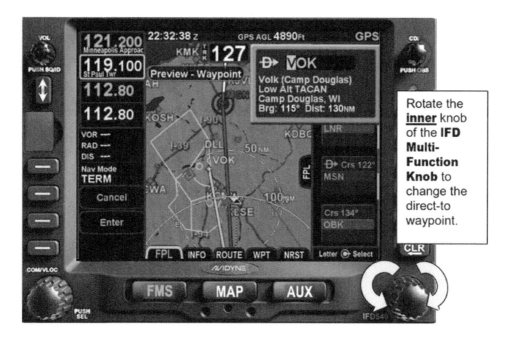

Figure 5 - 10 Entering a New Direct-To Waypoint

☑ After confirming that the new waypoint is correct, press the **ENTR** key twice to confirm it. You are now proceeding directly to the VOK VOR.

Figure 5 - 11 Confirming the Off-Route Direct-To Waypoint

Closing a Gap in the Flight Plan

Everything is going well now. You are on a good course to avoid the severe weather that was reported to be ahead. But, as you look at your revised flight plan, you immediately see a problem. The word **Gap** appears after the VOK waypoint. And, if you bring up the map page and look at your routing, you will see that your flight plan abruptly ends at VOK. There's nothing after that except a huge gap before Madison. If you don't make a change, your aircraft will reach VOK and just keep going in a straight line forever. That will not please your ATC controller.

Figure 5 - 12 Flight Plan Gap

Did you make a mistake? No, you simply haven't finished yet. ATC wanted to get you turned off course before you ran into the weather, so they didn't give you a complete clearance. And you wanted to comply quickly, so you accepted it without asking too many questions. But now it's time to clean things up.

You call ATC with the following request:

"Center, Cessna 1291S requests direct Madison after Volk."

They reply:

"Cessna 1291S, after Volk cleared direct to Madison."

So your task is simple: Remove the gap in the flight plan so you go direct to MSN after VOK.

Proceed as follows:

☑ Use the **IFD Multi-Function** knob to put the cyan edit cursor around the flight plan gap. You can also tap on the gap.

Figure 5 - 13 Selecting the Flight Plan Gap

☑ When the flight plan gap has been selected, the caption **Connect VOK & MSN** will appear next to the bottom line select key on the left side of the display.

☑ Press the line select key. The gap in the flight plan will disappear.

Figure 5 - 14 Removing the Gap

Note: You can close the gap in many cases by pressing the **CLR** key when the gap is selected. **CLR** can be used to delete any waypoint and it will also delete a gap in your flight plan. There are instances where the gaps cannot be cleared from the flightplan which will be addressed more in depth in Lesson 6 when discussing SIDs and STARs.

Figure 5 - 15 Flight Plan after Gap Is Closed

☑   Verify that the gap has been closed by using the line select key to select **View Cursor** and scrolling through the flight plan with the outer **IFD-Multi-Function** knob. The map will re-center as you select each waypoint. You will see that the VOK and MSN waypoints are now connected.

Figure 5 - 16 Reviewing the Flight Plan

Adding a Waypoint

Another common flight plan modification is the addition of a waypoint. This often happens due to ATC re-routes or to avoid weather or traffic. To see how this is done, we will add a new waypoint to the route that has already been programmed.

As we continue with our scenario, you are now flying directly to VOK, followed by MSN. But nothing is ever simple in the ATC world. You receive the following instructions:

> **"Cessna 1291S, Chicago Approach will not accept you on your current routing. After Madison, cleared direct Janesville, direct Northbrook, as filed."**

After a quick look at your charts you see that the new route requires a small change to your flight plan. You must insert new waypoint, JVL, between MSN and OBK.

You can do this by proceeding as follows:

- ☑ Press the **FMS** key and the **FPL** tab (if necessary) to display the **FMS FPL** Page.

- ☑ If necessary, tap on the **MAP** tab on the left side of the **FMS FPL** page to display a map next to the flight plan waypoints.

- ☑ Turn the outer **IFD Multi-Function** knob until the Insert cursor is between the MSN and OBK waypoints. You can also position the cursor by simply tapping between the two waypoints on the touch screen.

Figure 5 - 17 Positioning the Insert Cursor

☑ When the insert cursor is in the right spot, press the **ENTR** key twice. The first time you press **ENTR**, a dialog box will be displayed asking if you want to insert a new waypoint or to do something else. Pressing **ENTR** a second time confirms that you want a waypoint.

Figure 5 - 18 Inserting a New Waypoint

☑ After pressing **ENTR** the second time, a new waypoint box will appear between the MSN and OBK fixes. Enter the identifier of the new waypoint by turning the inner and outer **IFD Multi-Function** knobs. Or, you can tap the waypoint box to bring up the on-screen keyboard.

Note that your new route is displayed on the preview map while the new waypoint is being entered.

Lesson 5: Changing a Flight Plan

Figure 5 - 19 Entering the Waypoint Identifier

☑ Once the new waypoint ID has been entered, press the **ENTR** key to accept it. Your flight plan has been changed.

☑ Confirm the routing by using the cursor centered map to review it.

Figure 5 - 20 Accepting the Inserted Waypoint

Deleting Waypoints

Sometimes an in-flight re-route requires a waypoint to be deleted from a flight plan. Let's see how this is done.

You have now been cleared on a routing from your present position direct to VOK, then over MSN, JVL, and OBK. But ATC soon calls again:

"Cessna 1291S, Chicago Approach changed their minds. After Madison, cleared direct Northbrook, as filed."

The revised route requires the JVL waypoint, which you just added, to be deleted. Follow these steps:

☑ Turn the **IFD Multi-Function** knob to put the edit cursor around the JVL waypoint. Or, you can simply tap on the JVL waypoint.

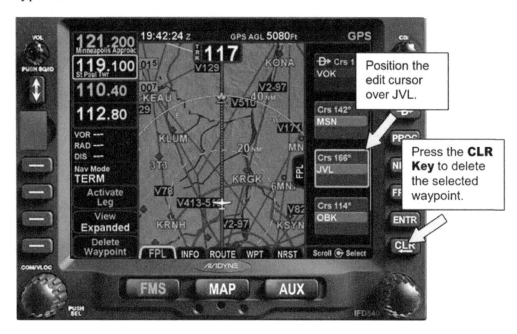

Figure 5 - 21 Deleting a Waypoint

☑ Press the **CLR** key. As soon as you do so the JVL waypoint will disappear from the flight plan.

Note that there is no "confirm" sequence when you are deleting a waypoint (unless you are deleting the current "to" waypoint). As soon as you press CLR, the waypoint is gone. Be sure you're deleting the right waypoint before you press the button!

☑ See that the waypoint has been deleted.

Figure 5 - 22 Flight Plan after Waypoint Deletion

Changing a Destination

What happens if you want to divert your flight to a different destination airport? How can you do that?

To the IFD, an airport is simply a special kind of a waypoint. You can add it and delete it just as you would with any other waypoint. On your flight plan it looks like a normal waypoint, except that it's usually the last one in the sequence.

With that in mind, there are several ways you could change your destination. Two of them are:

1. You could delete the old destination and add a new destination waypoint at the end of the flight plan.

2. You could simply add the new destination to the end of the flight plan and, if permitted by ATC, fly direct to the new destination. This method has the advantage of preserving the old destination in the flight plan so you could go back to it, "just in case."

Let's continue the scenario once again.

You are proceeding as before when ATC comes on the radio once again. They say:

> *"Cessna 1291S, Chicago Approach reports heavy thunderstorms at Midway Airport. No traffic is currently getting in, expect extensive holding until the airport reopens."*

You reply:

> *"Center, Cessna 1291S requests diversion to the Janesville airport. We'll wait it out on the ground."*

ATC answers:

> *"Roger Cessna 1291S. Cleared direct to the Janesville airport."*

Let's make this happen. We will use the second method suggested above.
 Lesson 5: Changing a Flight Plan

☑ Press the **FMS** key and the **FPL** tab (if necessary) to display the Flight Plan Page.

☑ Tap the **MAP** tab on the left side of the flight plan page (if necessary) to display a map next to the flight plan waypoints.

☑ Turn the **IFD Multi-Function** knob until the cursor is at the end of the flight plan, after the KMDW waypoint.

Figure 5 - 23 Positioning the Insert Cursor at the End of the Flight Plan

☑ Press the **ENTR** key twice to bring up a waypoint insertion box. When the box appears, enter KJVL, the identifier of the Janesville airport.

Figure 5 - 24 Entering the New Destination Waypoint

☑ Press the **Direct-To** key. Since the KJVL waypoint was just entered, it will be inside the edit cursor box and it will be the suggested direct-to waypoint. Press the **ENTR** key twice to accept it.

Figure 5 - 25 Activating the Direct-To Destination

☑ You are now proceeding direct to the KJVL airport.

Figure 5 - 26 Flight Plan to New Destination

IFD440/410 Differences

All the flight planning procedures that have been explored in this lesson work exactly the same way in the IFD440 and IFD410 as they did in the IFD540. The only difference is that the IFD4XX has a much smaller screen. That means that not as much of your flight plan is visible, and you have to scroll up and down more to review it. The map is smaller too, so not as much of your route is visible.

Figure 5 - 27 IFD440 Flight Plan MAP Tab Display

Lesson Review

This lesson has taught you the basics of editing your flight plans. The operations we talked about are:

Building Flight Plans

- Flight plans are built and edited on the FMS FPL page. You reach this page by pressing the FMS key and then selecting the FPL tab.

- Flight plans are built by adding waypoints to the end of the flight plan. New waypoints are added at the position of the insertion cursor, which should be positioned after the last waypoint.

- You can use the outer IFD Multi-Function knob to scroll the flight plan up and down the page and to reposition the cursor. You can also use the touch screen to perform these functions.

- Tapping on the MAP tab on the left side of the FMS FPL page splits the screen into two parts. The right side shows a list of your flight plan's waypoints, while the left side shows those same waypoints on a map. You can use the map to see the flight plan route as you build it.

Checking a Flight Plan

- You should thoroughly check each flight plan before you use it and any time you change it.

- Flight plans can be checked by looking at all the waypoints on the FMS FPL Page, and on a map under the MAP Tab on the FMS FPL Page. You should use both methods.

- It is easier to review the flight plan on the MAP Tab of the FMS FPL Page if you use the View Line Select Key to select the View Cursor option. Now you can scroll through the waypoint list with the outer IFD Multi-Function Knob and the map will re-center itself as each waypoint is selected.

- After a flight plan has been entered and checked you should activate it by pressing the Activate Flight Plan line select key. If you do not activate a flight plan the IFD will activate it automatically when you take off.

Lesson 5: Changing a Flight Plan

Going Direct to a Waypoint

- The Direct-To key is used to go directly to any waypoint on your flight plan. To do this, go to the FMS FPL page to display the flight plan, use the outer IFD Multi-Function knob to select the waypoint you want to go to, and press the Direct-To key. Confirm the action by pressing the ENTR key twice.

- You can also use the Direct-To key to go to a waypoint that's not on your current flight plan. Press the Direct-To key, and then use the inner and outer IFD Multi-Function knobs to change the identifier of the direct-to waypoint. Press the ENTR key twice to confirm. You can also use the on-screen keyboard to enter the waypoint ID.

- Going direct to an off-route waypoint can put gaps in your flight plan. It's important to take them out, because your aircraft will stop navigating when it reaches a gap and simply fly in a straight line. You can remove a gap by turning the outer IFD Multi-Function knob to put the cursor box around it, then press the "connect" line select key. You can also press the CLR key to close the gap.

Adding a Waypoint

- You can add a waypoint to a flight plan by using the outer IFD Multi-Function knob to move the cursor to the place where you want to insert the waypoint.

- After the cursor has been positioned, press the ENTR key twice to bring up the waypoint dialog box.

- Enter the waypoint ID in the usual fashion and press the ENTR key to confirm.

Deleting a Waypoint

- A flight plan waypoint can be deleted by rotating the outer IFD Multi-Function knob to move the Cursor box around it.

- After the cursor has been positioned, press the CLR key to delete the waypoint.

- You are not asked to confirm before the deletion occurs, so be sure that you're deleting the correct fix.

Changing the Destination

- To change your destination, add the new destination airport as a waypoint at the end of the flight plan. Then modify the flight plan as necessary to get to the new destination, or simply use the Direct-To key to go to it directly.

Lesson 6: Advanced Flight Plans

The previous lessons showed you how to build and edit simple flight plans using your IFD5XX/4XX. Now it's time to get a little more complicated.

In this lesson you will learn to incorporate airways, standard departures, and standard arrivals into your flight plans. You will also learn how to fly headings to intercept a radial of a waypoint, and how to fly a course which is offset a specified distance from your flight plan.

At the end of this lesson you will be thoroughly familiar with all the elements of flight plans and will be ready to start learning about holding patterns and instrument approaches.

Adding Airways to Flight Plans

This lesson will use the same scenario that was used in the previous one. But the flight plans will get a little more complicated.

The Scenario

You are once again at the St. Paul Downtown airport (KSTP), preparing for a trip to the Chicago Midway airport (KMDW). You receive the following clearance from Minneapolis Clearance Delivery:

> *"Cessna 1291S, you are cleared from the St. Paul Downtown airport to the Chicago Midway airport via the PRESS intersection, Victor 2, Nodine, Victor 170, Dells, Janesville, V24, UMUZI, climb and maintain 5000, squawk 1234."*

Let's get ready to fly this trip.

Start the IFD540 Simulator and Display the FPL Page

As before, before you start your flight you will build the flight plan on the **FMS FPL** page.

- ☑ Start the IFD540 simulator program on your iPad.

- ☑ Press the **FMS** rocker. This will display one of the FMS pages. (It may be displayed already when you start the simulator.)

- ☑ Press the left side of the **FMS** rocker. This will sequentially select the tabs at the bottom of the FMS pages. Stop when you have selected the FPL tab.

- ☑ If necessary, open the split-screen flight plan map by tapping on the **MAP** tab on the left side of the display.

Build the New Flight Plan

This flight plan is very similar to the one you built previously. The big difference is that it includes airways instead of point-to-point waypoints.

To build it, do the following:

- ☑ Enter the origin airport, **KSTP**, as you did in the previous lesson.

- ☑ Enter the first waypoint, **PRESS**.

The flight plan should look like the one in the following figure:

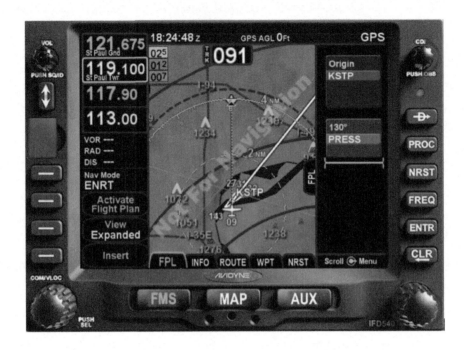

Figure 6 - 1 Start of a New Flight Plan

Now it's time to enter the airway, V2. All high and low altitude airways are stored in the IFD's database. Each is defined by a string of waypoints. But you can't just join an airway anywhere. Airways are like superhighways; you have to get on at an on-ramp and get off at an off-ramp. When building a flight plan, you always have to join an airway by getting on at an "on-waypoint" and getting off at an "off-waypoint."

The new flight plan is already built as far as the PRESS intersection. A look at a low-altitude chart shows that V2 goes through PRESS. So PRESS will serve as our on-waypoint to V2.

Perform the following steps:

☑ Make sure that the insertion cursor is located under the PRESS waypoint.

☑ Press the **ENTR** key. A blue WAYPOINT dialog box will appear.

☑ In the last exercise, at this point you pressed **ENTR** again to add another waypoint. But this time you want to enter an airway. Turn the outer IFD Multi-Function knob to move the cursor down until V2 is highlighted in blue. You could also use the touch screen to perform the same functions.

Note that there are several other airways that are available. Each of these go through the PRESS intersection. You could select any of them if you wanted to go a different direction.

When you select airway V2, the map portion of the screen will change to the Preview – Airway view. This view shows the airway that you have selected on the map, helping you to ensure that it's the right one.

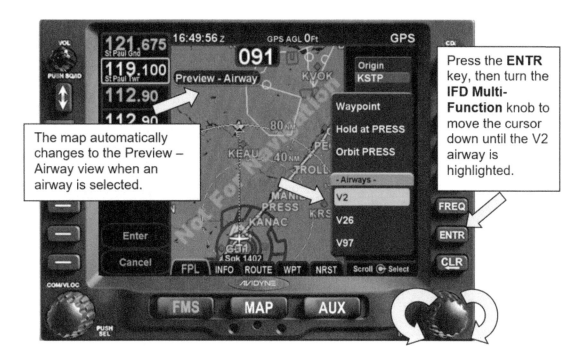

Figure 6 - 2 Selecting an Airway

☑ When V2 is highlighted, press the **ENTR** key again to select it. This defines the airway's "on-waypoint". Another dialog box will appear, asking for your exit point, or "off-waypoint."

☑ Use the **IFD Multi-Function** knob to move up and down a list of all the waypoints that define the airway. As you do so, the preview map will change to show the portion of the airway that you have selected. Move the cursor down until **ODI**, your next waypoint, is highlighted.

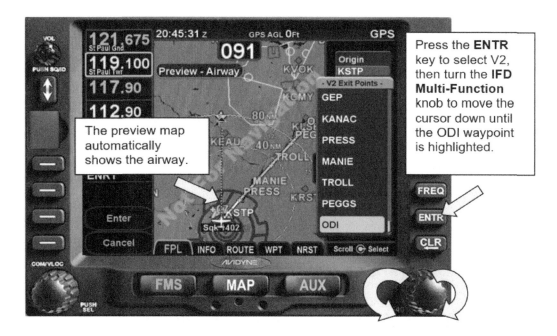

Figure 6 - 3 Selecting the Airway Exit Point

Lesson 6: Advanced Flight Plans

☑ Press the **ENTR** key. This will select ODI as the exit waypoint. The airway and all its waypoints between PRESS and ODI have been added to the flight plan. You can see them in the waypoint list.

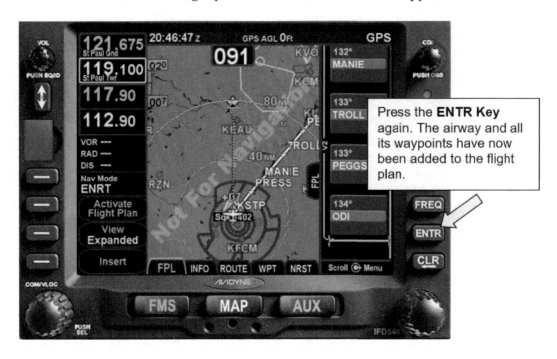

Figure 6 - 4 Confirming the Airway

After ODI, your clearance was V170 to the DLL waypoint. You can add that to your flight plan using the same procedure you used for V2.

☑ With the insertion cursor located under the ODI waypoint, press the **ENTR** key.

☑ Use the outer **IFD Multi-Function** knob to highlight V170.

☑ Press the **ENTR** key again to select V170.

Figure 6 - 5 Selecting the Next Airway

Lesson 6: Advanced Flight Plans

☑ Use the **IFD Multi-Function** knob to highlight DLL, the exit waypoint.

☑ Press the **ENTR** key to add V170 and DLL to the flight plan.

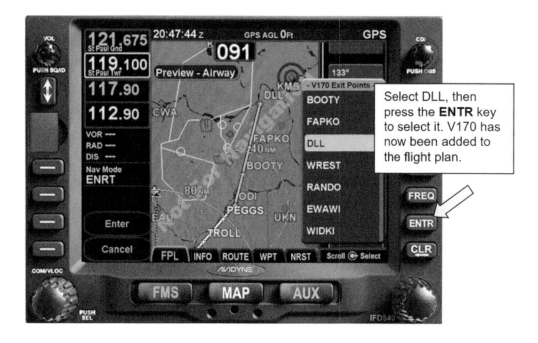

Figure 6 - 6 Confirming the Next Exit Point

☑ Finish the flight plan by adding JVL, V24, UMUZI, and KMDW. Use the same procedure that you used above.

The completed flight plan should look like the following figure:

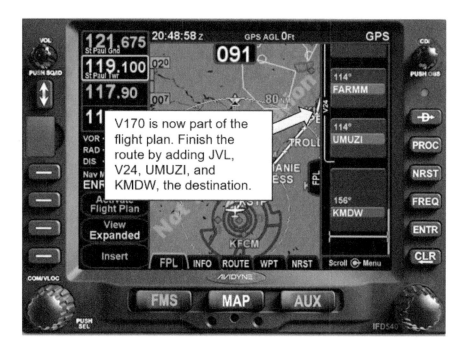

Figure 6 - 7 Completed Flight Plan with Airways

Check the Flight Plan

Remember that no flight plan is complete until it has been checked thoroughly.

☑ As you did before, press the **View** line select key on the left side of the display repeatedly until the **View Cursor** caption is displayed. Then turn the outer **IFD Multi-Function** knob to scroll through each waypoint of the flight plan. As you do so, the map will change to be centered on the current waypoint. Check all the waypoints against a chart to make sure they are correct.

Figure 6 - 8 Reviewing the Flight Plan with View Cursor

☑ After you check the waypoints, press the **View** line select key repeatedly until the **View Compact** caption is displayed. This option changes your flight plan display to show the airway entry and exit points only, and not all the intermediate waypoints. (Those waypoints are still in the route, they're just not shown on the screen.) This makes it a little easier to see the flight plan in the same way that your clearance was issued.

☑ Press the **Activate Flight Plan** line select key after you have finished checking your flight plan.

Figure 6 - 9 The View Compact Mode

Standard Arrivals and Departures

Standard arrivals and departures are often used when you are flying in or out of large airports, or reliever airports that are located near large hubs. They are used to organize the flow of traffic and generally make things easier for the ATC system. Fortunately, most arrivals and departures are included in the IFD's database.

> **Note:** "Vector" departures (those that rely on radar vectors and do not include any routing information), are <u>not</u> in the databases.

The Scenario

You are at the St. Paul Downtown airport (KSTP) again, preparing for a trip to the Chicago Midway airport (KMDW). This time you receive a more "interesting" clearance:

> *"Cessna 1291S, you are cleared from the St. Paul Downtown airport to the Chicago Midway airport via the ZMBRO7 departure, Nodine (ODI) transition, direct Davenport (CVA) , MOTIF6 arrival, climb and maintain 5000, squawk 1234. Expect runway 27 for departure."*

This is a pretty roundabout routing, but you know that there are thunderstorms northwest of Chicago so it's probably the best routing you can get.

Let's see how we can put this together in the IFD.

Review the Departure

You have been assigned the ZMBRO7 departure, Nodine transition. The first thing to do is to check your charts. The departure is shown below.

Note that this departure includes an initial heading which depends on the runway you are using, then a radar vector segment, followed by a standard routing.

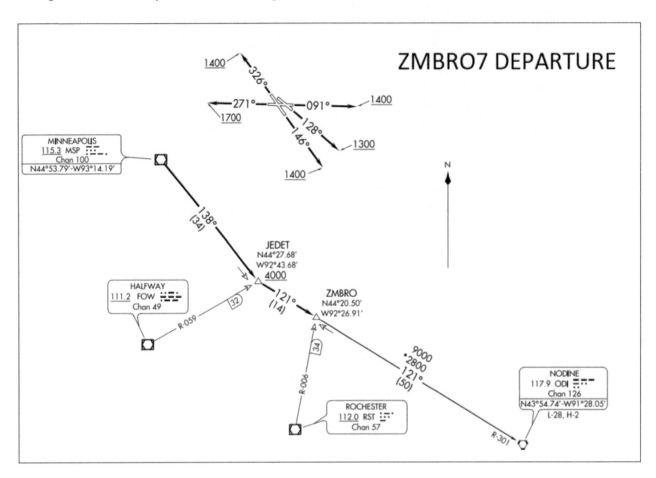

Figure 6 - 10 ZMBRO Seven Departure, Graphic View

ZMBRO SEVEN DEPARTURE

DEPARTURE ROUTE DESCRIPTON

TAKEOFF RUNWAY 9: Climb heading 091° to 1400 for RADAR vectors to MSP VOR/DME then on MSP R-138 to cross JEDET INT/MSP 34 DME, at or above 4000; then on ODI R-301 to ZMBRO INT/ODI 50 DME, thence . . . .

TAKEOFF RUNWAY 13: Climb heading 128° to 1300 for RADAR vectors to MSP VOR/DME then on MSP R-138 to cross JEDET INT/MSP 34 DME, at or above 4000; then on ODI R-301 to ZMBRO INT/ODI 50 DME, thence . . . .

TAKEOFF RUNWAY 14: Climb heading 146° to 1400 for RADAR vectors to MSP VOR/DME then on MSP R-138 to cross JEDET INT/MSP 34 DME, at or above 4000; then on ODI R-301 to ZMBRO INT/ODI 50 DME, thence . . . .

TAKEOFF RUNWAY 27: Climb heading 271° to 1700 for RADAR vectors to MSP VOR/DME then on MSP R-138 to cross JEDET INT/MSP 34 DME, at or above 4000; then on ODI R-301 to ZMBRO INT/ODI 50 DME, thence . . . .

TAKEOFF RUNWAY 32: Climb heading 326° to 1400 for RADAR vectors to MSP VOR/DME then on MSP R-138 to cross JEDET INT/MSP 34 DME, at or above 4000; then on ODI R-301 to ZMBRO INT/ODI 50 DME, thence . . . .

. . . .on assigned transition or route. Expect clearance to filed altitude/flight level 10 (ten) minutes after departure.

Figure 6 - 11 ZMBRO Seven Departure, Text View

Start the IFD540 Simulator and Display the FPL Page

Before you start your flight you will build the flight plan on the **FMS FPL** page. Do the following:

☑ Start the IFD540 simulator program on your iPad.

☑ Press the **FMS** rocker. This will display one of the FMS pages. (It may be displayed already when you start the simulator.)

☑ Press the left side of the **FMS** rocker. This will sequentially select the tabs at the bottom of the FMS pages. Stop when you have selected the FPL tab.

☑ If necessary, close the split-screen flight plan map by tapping on the vertical **FPL** tab on the display.

Set the Departure Runway

This flight plan starts with a standard departure, which includes a different initial segment for each runway.

> **CAUTION:** It is very important to enter the correct runway in the flight plan. At large airports, putting the wrong runway into your flight plan will cause the wrong transition waypoints for the departure procedure to be loaded, which can lead to conflicts with traffic from adjacent runways. Always be sure that your departure runway is correct. Be sure to change it if you receive a last-minute runway change after you taxi out. The transition waypoints will change when the runway is changed.

To enter the departure runway, do the following:

☑   Enter the origin airport, KSTP, as you did in the previous lesson.

☑   Turn the inner **IFD Multi-Function** knob until the **Rwy** box of the origin airport is highlighted.

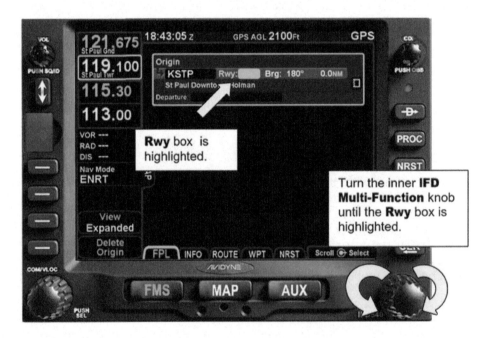

Figure 6 - 12 Selecting the Runway Box

☑   Press the **ENTR** key. A box showing a list of departure runways will appear.

☑   Turn the either the inner or outer **IFD Multi-Function** knob until runway 27 is highlighted in blue.

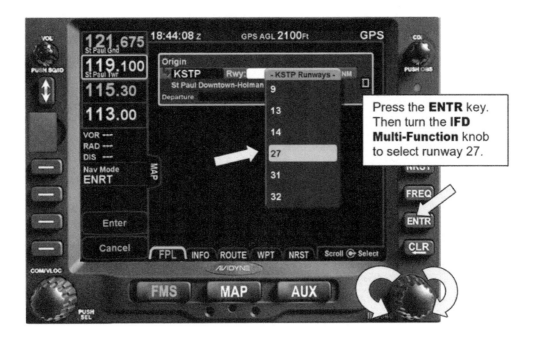

Figure 6 - 13 Selecting the Departure Runway

☑ Press the **ENTR** key again. Runway 27 has now been set as the departure runway.

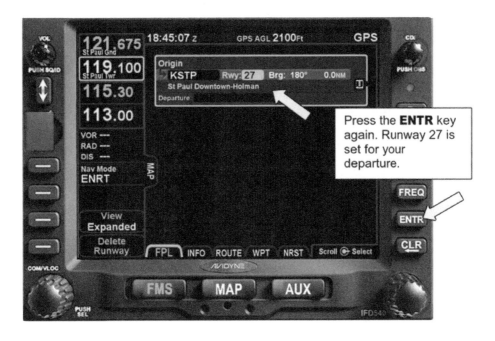

Figure 6 - 14 Completed Departure Runway

Program the Standard Departure

Now that the departure runway has been set, you can add the departure procedure to your flight plan. This is similar to the way that the runway was selected.

☑ Turn the inner **IFD Multi-Function** knob until the **Departure** box of the origin airport is highlighted.

Lesson 6: Advanced Flight Plans

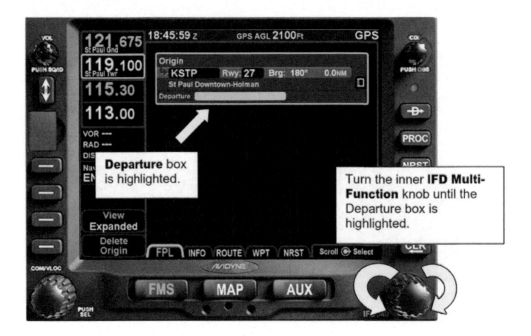

Figure 6 - 15 Selecting the Departure Box

☑ Press the **ENTR** key. A list of the standard departures for the KSTP airport will be displayed.

Figure 6 - 16 Displaying the List of Departures

☑ Use the outer **IFD Multi-Function** knob to scroll down until the ZMBRO7 departure is highlighted. Press the **ENTR** key to select it.

☑ A list of transitions will appear. Select the **ODI** transition and press the **ENTR** key.

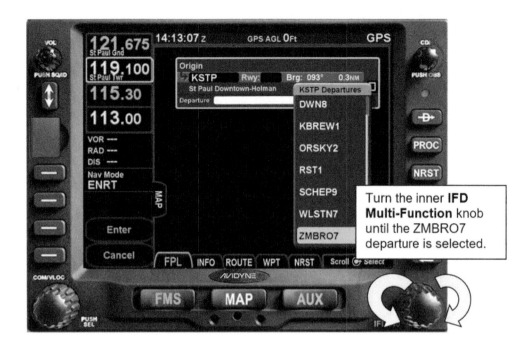

Figure 6 - 17 Selecting the Departure Procedure

☑ Press the **ENTR** key. The ZMBRO7 departure has now been added to your flight plan. Review it to confirm that it includes all the segments shown on the chart: An initial heading off the runway with an altitude restriction, a radar vector segment, and a defined route after the MSP VOR.

> **Note:** Some departures have multiple transition routes. If there is more than one possible transition, another box is displayed after you have selected a departure. This box shows all the possible transitions and allows you to select one of them.

Figure 6 - 18 Departure Procedure Added to Flight Plan

Changing or Deleting a Departure Runway

Follow these steps to change a departure runway:

- ☑ Use the inner **IFD Multi-Function** knob to select the **Rwy** box on the origin airport.

- ☑ Press the **ENTR** key. A list of runways will be displayed.

- ☑ Use the inner or outer **IFD Multi-Function** knob to select the new runway.

- ☑ Press the **ENTR** key.

If a standard departure has been loaded, it will automatically change to reflect the new runway assignment.

To delete the departure runway entirely:

- ☑ Use the inner **IFD Multi-Function** knob to select the **Rwy** box on the origin airport.

- ☑ Press the **CLR** key.

The departure runway will be removed and all departure segments associated with it will be deleted.

Changing or Deleting a Standard Departure

Changing your departure is very similar to changing your runway:

- ☑ Use the inner **IFD Multi-Function** knob to select the **Departure** box on the origin airport.

- ☑ Press the **ENTR** key. A list of departures will be displayed.

- ☑ Use the inner or outer **IFD Multi-Function** knob to select the new departure.

- ☑ Press the **ENTR** key.

- ☑ Press the **ENTR** key again to confirm the change.

To delete the departure entirely:

- ☑ Use the inner **IFD Multi-Function** knob to select the **Departure** box on the origin airport.

- ☑ Press the **CLR** key.

- ☑ Press the **ENTR** key to confirm the deletion.

The standard departure will be removed.

Adding a Standard Arrival

Now that you have added the departure runway and procedure to the flight plan, you can move ahead to the rest of the clearance.

After the ZMBRO7 departure ends at the Nodine (ODI) VOR, your clearance reads "direct Davenport (CVA), MO-TIF6 arrival, Midway Airport." The first thing to do is to look at the chart for the arrival, which is shown below.

This chart has several different arrival transitions. You will be coming in over the CVA VOR, which is west of the Midway Airport. The arrival is the same no matter which runway you are landing on.

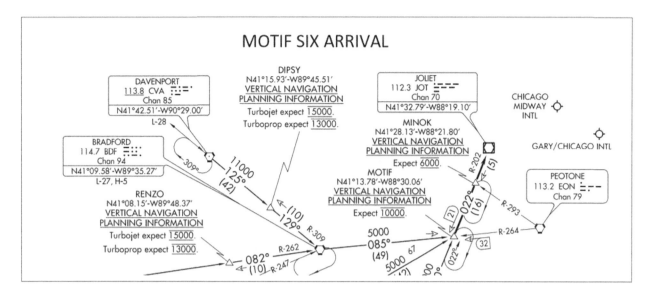

Figure 6 - 19 MOTIF Six Arrival

You should have already put the KSTP origin airport and the ZMBRO7 departure in your flight plan. The ZMBRO7 route ends at the Nodine VOR (ODI). Let's pick it up from there:

☑ Enter the next waypoint, **CVA**, at the end of the flight plan.

☑ Enter the arrival airport, **KMDW**.

You are not cleared direct from CVA to KMDW; there's a standard arrival between the two. But the airport has to be put in the flight plan <u>before</u> the arrival. You need the airport in order to find a list of arrivals.

Your flight plan should look like the following illustration:

Figure 6 - 20 Flight Plan Before Arrival Is Added

Lesson 6: Advanced Flight Plans

Now it's time to add the arrival route. This is done in much the same way as the departure was programmed.

☑ Turn the inner **IFD Multi-Function** knob to highlight the **Arr** box on the arrival airport (KMDW) waypoint.

☑ Press the **ENTR** key. A list of KMDW arrivals will appear.

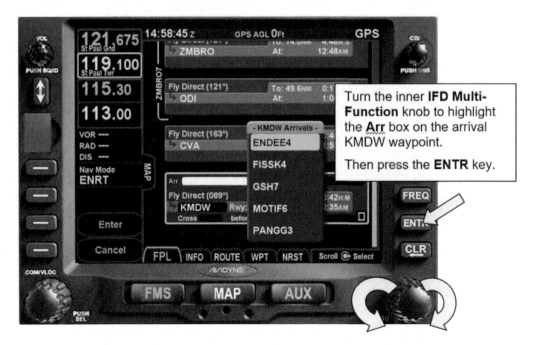

Figure 6 - 21 Displaying the List of Arrivals

☑ Turn the inner or outer **IFD Multi-Function** knob to highlight the MOTIF6 arrival.

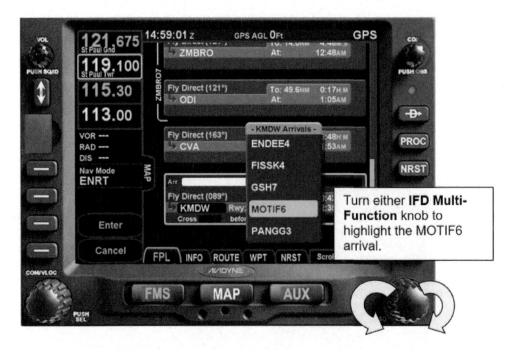

Figure 6 - 22 Selecting the MOTIF6 Arrival

☑ Press the **ENTR** key to select the arrival. This arrival has several possible transitions. You have to select one of them, so a list of transitions now appears.

Lesson 6: Advanced Flight Plans

☑ Turn the inner or outer **IFD Multi-Function** knob to highlight the CVA transition.

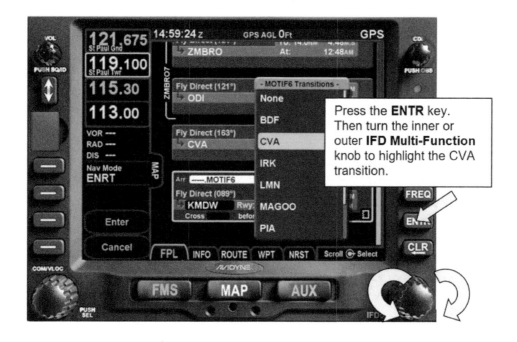

Figure 6 - 23 Selecting the Transition Route

☑ Press the **ENTR** key to select the transition. The entire MOTIF6 arrival has now been added to your flight plan.

Figure 6 - 24 MOTIF6 CVA Transition Added to Flight Plan

☑ Tap on the **MAP** tab to open the preview map. Use the **View Cursor** mode to check the arrival route. Ensure that it includes all the waypoints shown on the chart.

☑ Press the **Activate Flight Plan** line select key to activate your flight plan.

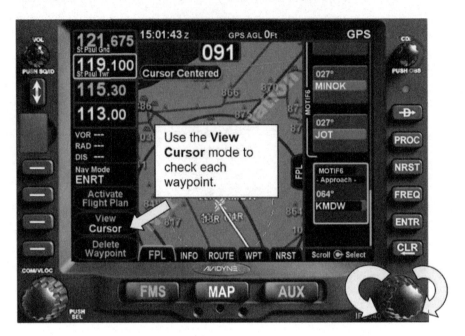

Figure 6 - 25 Using View Cursor to Check the Flight Plan

The arrival transition you chose was over CVA which, conveniently, was the last waypoint before KMDW. The IFD was smart enough to see that the route was continuous, so it closed the gap and did not include CVA twice. If you had selected a different transition there would have been a gap between CVA and the first arrival fix. You would have had to close this before using the plan.

Selecting the Arrival Runway

It is not uncommon to find standard arrivals that have different routings for different arrival runways. This is often the case at larger airports. For example, look at the SPUDS4 arrival at KPHL, which "forks" in two different directions. The fork in use will depend on whether traffic is landing to the east or to the west.

If you are flying an arrival like this, you must add the arrival runway to your flight plan. This is done by entering the runway into the **Rwy** box on the arrival airport waypoint. The procedure is the same as you used for entering the departure runway on your origin airport.

You often do not know the landing runway until you arrive in the terminal area. Therefore, you can't program the full arrival during your initial pre-flight setup – you must add the runway as soon as you find out what it is. Furthermore, you must enter the arrival runway <u>before</u> you program the instrument approach procedure.

> **CAUTION:** If you do not add the runway to your flight plan, or if you add it after you program the instrument approach, you could miss some of the waypoints that are part of the arrival procedure. This could cause you to fly off course and incur an ATC deviation. Always review the entire arrival procedure to ensure it matches the chart.

Headings to Intercept a Radial

Now the departure procedure, the short en-route segment, and the standard arrival into Midway Airport have all been programmed into your IFD. You have checked the flight plan thoroughly to make sure that it is correct. The initial part of the flight plan should look like the following screen. You are departing runway 27 and using the ZMBRO7 departure procedure.

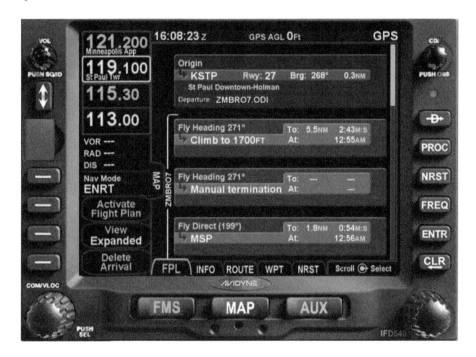

Figure 6 - 26 Flight Plan Showing Departure Procedure

You are ready to go flying. Let's continue our scenario:

The IFD540 simulator is already set up from the previous paragraphs. You just have to begin the flight. Do the following:

☑ Activate the flight plan if you haven't done so already.

☑ Press the **MAP** rocker under the display screen. This will display the moving map page so you can watch your flight.

After takeoff, the first part of the ZMBRO7 departure from runway 27 says that you should maintain a heading of 268 degrees. That's part of the procedure stored in the IFD, as shown in the flight plan. The unit will give you guidance in the initial part of your climb.

Figure 6 - 27 Initial Leg of Departure

After you reach an altitude of 1700 feet on the initial climb segment, the departure procedure says that you should expect radar vectors. The IFD can't help you with that – in a real aircraft you would just steer yourself, following ATC's instructions. At some point, however, you'll be turned loose to navigate on your own.

Shortly after takeoff you receive the following clearance:

"Cessna 1291S, turn left heading 185, intercept the Minneapolis (MSP) 138 degree radial, continue the ZMBRO Seven departure."

Now your task is to intercept the first leg of the departure, defined by a radial off the MSP VOR. Proceed as follows:

☑ Press the **FMS** key and the **FPL** tab (if necessary) to display the FMS FPL Page.

☑ If necessary, tap on the **MAP** tab on the left side of the FMS FPL page to display a map next to the flight plan waypoints.

☑ Turn the outer **IFD Multi-Function** knob until the cursor box is around the JEDET waypoint. You can also position the cursor by simply tapping on the JEDET waypoint.

> **Note:** Even though you have been cleared to intercept a radial from MSP, you must select the waypoint at the <u>end</u> of the MSP leg. That is because when you use GPS you always navigate "to" a waypoint, never "from" a waypoint.

☑ After JEDET has been highlighted, press the line select key next to the **Activate Leg** caption on the left side of the display screen. This tells the IFD 540 that you want to activate the leg between MSP and JEDET.

Figure 6 - 28 Selecting the Second Departure Leg

☑   A green box will appear, asking if you really want to activate the JEDET leg. Press the **ENTR** key to confirm.

Figure 6 - 29 Activating the Second Departure Leg

Your simulated aircraft will turn to begin the intercept as soon as you confirm the new active leg. The fact that the MSP-JEDET leg appears in magenta confirms that it is now active. When the aircraft reaches this leg it will turn again and track along it.

Lesson 6: Advanced Flight Plans

Figure 6 - 30 Flight Plan Set Up for Intercept

Intercepting and tracking the MSP radial of a published departure is straightforward because the route is already part of a procedure included in the IFD's database. But what if you want to do something a little more difficult? How would you track a "random" radial that's not part of a flight plan already? Let's find out.

As you approach the MSP-JEDET leg, ATC calls again:

> **"Cessna 1291S, on your present heading intercept the Nodine (ODI) 305 degree radial, then continue as filed."**

So now you need to intercept and track a radial from the Nodine VOR (ODI). You could always tune in the VOR, put the IFD in VLOC mode, and track it manually. But it would be much better if you could program the radial into your existing flight plan. And you can.

You can program the IFD to track any radial into any waypoint. The waypoint does not have to be a VOR; you can select any waypoint and track to it any direction you would like.

Do the following:

☑ Use the outer **IFD Multi-Function** knob to select the waypoint you'll be tracking to: ODI.

☑ After ODI has been highlighted, press the line select key next to the **Activate Leg** caption on the left side of the display screen.

☑ Press the **ENTR** key to confirm the new leg.

Figure 6 - 31 Selecting and Activating the TO Waypoint

The leg between ZMBRO and ODI is now activated, making ODI your current "to" waypoint. The display should look like the one shown below. You can't see the ZMBRO-ODI leg because it's too far away and is off the screen.

Figure 6 - 32 TO Waypoint Set to ODI

But you're not finished yet; you need to set up the ODI 305 radial, as specified in your clearance.

Continue as follows:

☑ Press the **OBS** knob in the upper right corner of the IFD. The green GPS caption above it will flash a few times and then change to OBS. That means that your IFD is now in OBS Mode, which means that you can select your own radials to waypoints.

☑ Turn the **OBS** knob. As you do so, the cyan Crs number will change. Keep turning until **125** is displayed. You will see the radial swing into the display window. It's magenta, so it's the current leg.

Note: You are dialing in 125, not 305. ATC cleared you to the 305 degree radial of ODI. Remember that radials are "from" bearings, but you must navigate "to" ODI. Therefore, you have to set 125, which is the reciprocal of 305.

Note: Your aircraft will behave differently than the IFD simulator. You will probably have an external navigation indicator, such as an HSI or a CDI. If you do, you will set the inbound radial by using the course selection knob on your indicator. You only use the OBS knob on the IFD to select the course if you do not have an external indicator. This is unlikely.

Figure 6 - 33 Setting the Inbound Radial

The simulated aircraft will now intercept and track the radial you have selected.

Figure 6 - 34 OBS Mode

You can press the OBS knob at any time to get out of OBS mode. You will go back to GPS mode, and the aircraft will go back to tracking the current leg of your flight plan.

When you reach the waypoint you are tracking to, the IFD will automatically go back to GPS mode. It will start tracking the next leg of the flight plan.

Figure 6 - 35 Tracking the Selected Radial

Course Offsets

Another handy tool is the IFD's ability to "offset" a course line. This means that, instead of flying down the center of the flight plan legs as you normally would, you can tell the IFD to fly a specified number of miles to the right or left of course. This could be useful if, for example, you want to make a temporary deviation around weather or a restricted area.

Let's continue with the scenario to see how this would work.

You continue on your flight until you pass the ODI waypoint. You then see a large bumpy-looking cumulous cloud ahead. Flying through it would give your passengers a very bad ride.

You call center:

> **"Center, Cessna 1291S requests a temporary deviation 5 miles right of course to avoid some weather."**

Your request is approved. Set up the IFD to fly the deviation as follows:

- ☑ Be sure that the simulated aircraft has indeed crossed ODI and the IFD is now in GPS mode. **(Course offsets don't work when you are in OBS mode.)** Speed up the simulator if necessary to get past ODI quickly.

- ☑ On the FMS FPL page, use the outer **IFD Multi-Function** knob to select the CVA waypoint. (You must select CVA because it is the current "to" waypoint. The "to" waypoint must be selected in order for the offset route caption in the next step to appear.)

- ☑ Press the **Offset Route** line select key on the left side of the display.

Figure 6 - 36 Selecting the Leg to Offset

- ☑ The caption on the line select key will change to **Confirm 0.0 NM**. This is the IFD's way of asking you how far you would like to offset your course.

Figure 6 - 37 The Offset Route Distance Box

☑ Turn the **IFD Multi-Function** knob to change the offset distance from 0.0 to **Right 5.0 NM**.

The outer knob controls whole miles, while the inner one controls tenths of miles. Right or left of course is controlled by turning the knob down to zero and then continuing to turn. The right/left indication will change and the offs et distance will start rising again.

Figure 6 - 38 Setting the Offset Distance

☑ Press the **ENTR** key to confirm the offset distance. A dashed magenta line will appear, showing the offset distance on the map. The simulated aircraft will turn to intercept the offset track.

Note: Offset courses usually continue along your flight plan for all subsequent waypoints. That is, the offset will automatically go around corners and follow the turns in your flight plan. However, in this case, the CVA waypoint is the beginning of a standard arrival route. You cannot offset arrivals, so the offset will stop when the aircraft reaches CVA.

Figure 6 - 39 Confirming the Offset

☑ To cancel the offset, press the **line select key** next to the **Offset Route** caption on the left side of the display screen.

Figure 6 - 40 Cancelling the Offset

Lesson 6: Advanced Flight Plans

☑   A new set of **line select key** captions will appear. Press the key next to the **Delete Offset** caption.

Figure 6 - 41 Confirming the Offset Cancellation

The course offset is now deleted. The aircraft will turn back to intercept and track its original course.

Figure 6 - 42 Flight Plan after Cancellation of Course Offset

Using "Rubber Band" Mode to Change a Flight Plan

Another way to offset a flight plan leg is to use "rubber band" mode. This method allows you to graphically change the flight plan directly on the IFD display. You simply use your finger to drag the current leg to a new position.

To use the rubber band method of altering a flight plan, do the following:

☑ Go to the **MAP** tab on the IFD display.

☑ Place your finger on the leg to be rubber-banded. Hold it there for at least two seconds. The leg will turn cyan.

☑ Drag your finger to the position on the map where you want a new waypoint to be inserted in your flight plan. If you drag it to an existing intersection or navaid that fix will be added to the flight plan. Otherwise a new rubber band waypoint will be added.

☑ A confirmation dialog box will appear. Press the **ENTR** key to accept the new waypoint, or the **CLR** key to reject it.

The new rubber band waypoint will be added to the flight plan between the two fixes which define the leg that was changed. If the current leg was rubber banded the rubber band waypoint will become the new TO waypoint and the leg between the FROM waypoint and the new TO waypoint will become the current leg. The aircraft will turn to intercept it. Use the Direct button if you want to go direct to the new waypoint.

Figure 6 - 43 Using Rubber Band Mode to Offset a Flight Plan Leg

Enroute Vertical Navigation

The IFD will provide vertical guidance during descents using either a predetermined descent rate (in FPM) or a predetermined descent angle (in degrees) as the path basis. The pilot can set a waypoint altitude constraint and the IFD will provide an indication of when to start the descent (Top of Descent – TOD) and will provide vertical guidance to reach the altitude constraint using the selected descent rate or descent angle. The altitude constraint will be shown using standard symbology: the constraint altitude will be shown with a single line below it for "at or above", a single line above it for "at or below", and a line both above and below for "at". An altitude block can also be set and will be shown as the upper altitude over the lower altitude with a line both on top and underneath the two altitudes.

Refer to Chapter 11 for setting preferences for Path Basis Descent Rate versus Decent Angle.

Descents using VNAV

This lesson assumes that you have already set your preferences for VNAV Path Basis as previously referenced.

To learn about enroute VNAV, imagine that you are flying VFR from the Double Eagle Airport in Albuquerque, NM (KAEG) to Wichita, KS (KICT). Your cruise altitude is 11,500'. For your descent into Wichita, you want to be at 3500' before you enter the Wichita Class C airspace so you set up a constraint to cross 15nm before KICT at 3500 so the IFD will provide the desired VNAV guidance.

- ☑ Touch the KICT leg on the flight plan.

- ☑ Touch "Cross" to set distance from waypoint (in this case KICT) for the altitude constraint. Set to the desired value using the pop-up keypad, and then press the enter key.

- ☑ Touch the next field to bring up a drop down menu. Select "at", and then press the ENTR key.

- ☑ Touch the next field to set the altitude "3500" using the pop-up keypad, and then press the ENTR key.

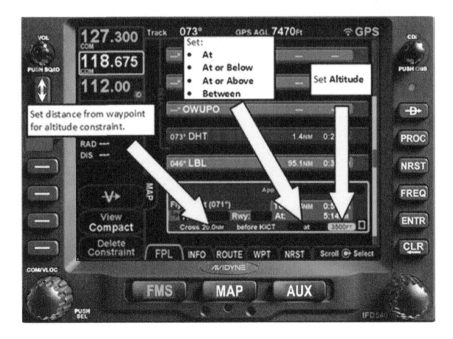

Figure 6 - 44 Setting Altitude Constraint

Inbound to KICT, on the MAP display, you will see the TOD descent point symbol (a green circle) appear indicating the point where a descent should be initiated. 20nm from the TOD symbol, the altitude constraint will be displayed as a magenta circle with an altitude next to it. If the pilot follows the guidance provided, the aircraft will be at 3500' at 20nm from KICT. The guidance provided will be based on the settings made during configuration of the Enroute VNAV (Descent Rate or Descent Angle).

As you approach close the TOD point, the IFD will provide a 9 second count down advisory followed by a "Descend Now" advisory.

☑ When the IFD provides the "Descend Now" advisory, touch the "Vertical Direct To" button next to the line select keys. Vertical guidance will now be provided. For IFD models with SVS, HDI and VDI guidance is provided for the descent on the SVS page. This guidance will terminate at the end of the descent.

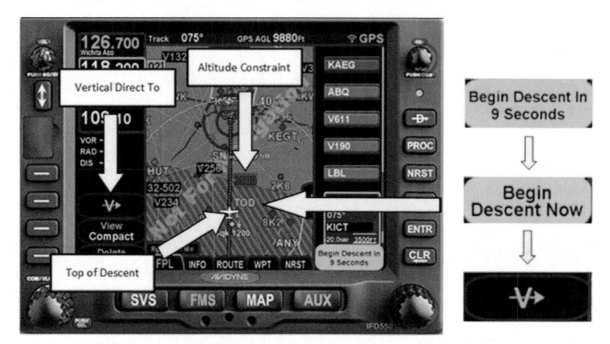

Figure 6 - 45 VNAV Pre-Descent Sequence

☑ The IFD will provide descent guidance until reaching the bottom of the descent at which point VNAV will be terminated.

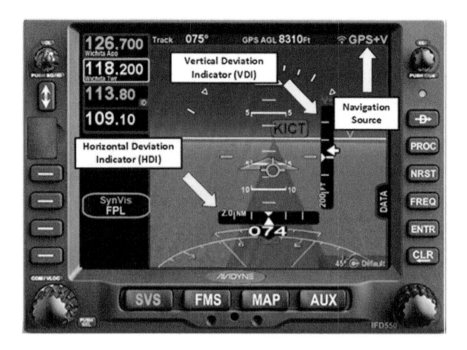

Figure 6 - 46 VNAV Guidance on SVS Page (IFD550/545)

☑ When VNAV is terminated, an advisory will be shown on the display. It will display on the FMS Map and the SVS page.

Figure 6 - 47 VNAV Terminated Advisory

IFD440/410 Differences

All the flight planning procedures that have been explored in this lesson work exactly the same way in the IFD440 and IFD410 as they do in the IFD540 and IFD550. The only difference is that the IFD4XX has a much smaller screen.

Figure 6 – 48 IFD440 Flight Plan Display

Lesson Review

This lesson has taught you some advanced flight plan features. The operations that were discussed are:

Adding Airways to Flight Plans

- All high and low altitude airways are stored in the IFD's internal database.

- Airways are similar to superhighways: You have to get on and off them at specified points. When you include an airway in a flight plan you must start at an "on" waypoint and end at an "off" waypoint.

- Adding an airway to a flight plan is done in four steps:

  1. Add the "on" waypoint to the flight plan.

  2. While the insert cursor is position after the "on" waypoint, press the ENTR key to display a list of airways that cross that point.

  3. Use the IFD Multi-Function knob or the touch screen to select the airway. Press the ENTR key to confirm.

  4. A list of "off" waypoints will appear. Select the appropriate one and press the ENTR key to confirm.

All the airway's waypoints between the "on" and "off" points will be added to the flight plan.

- The Preview – Airway mode of the FPL MAP screen shows you a preview of the airway while it is being added to your flight plan.

- You can use the **Compact** mode of the flight plan page to view airways without seeing all the intermediate waypoints.

- *It is very important that you check the programmed airway against your charts.* You can use the Cursor Centered mode of the FPL MAP screen to do this.

Lesson 6: Advanced Flight Plans

Standard Arrivals and Departures

- Like airways, most standard arrivals and departures are stored in the IFD's internal database.

- The exception to this rule is "vector only" departures, which generally include altitude restrictions but do not include specified routes. These departures are <u>not</u> included in the database.

- Many departures have different routings depending on which runway is used. The departure runway should be specified before the departure itself is added to the flight plan. If the runway is changed prior to departure, the runway in the flight plan must be changed as well. This will change the runway-dependent legs of the departure procedure.

- **Failure to select the correct departure runway could cause conflicts with other traffic.**

- The following procedure is used to add a standard departure:

  1. Use the IFD Multi-Function knob or the touch screen to highlight the Rwy box of the origin airport. Press the ENTR key to display a runway list.

  2. Select the departure runway and press the ENTR key to confirm it.

  3. Use the IFD Multi-Function knob or the touch screen to highlight the Departure box of the origin airport. Press the ENTR key to display a list of departures.

  4. Select the departure and press the ENTR key to confirm it.

  5. A list of departure transitions may be displayed. If so, select the appropriate one and press the ENTR key to confirm it.

All the waypoints associated with the departure will be added to your flight plan.

- The departure runway can be deleted by selecting the Rwy box and then pressing the CLR key. It can be changed by selecting the Rwy box and pressing the ENTR key to display the runway list.

- The departure can be deleted by selecting the Departure box and then pressing the CLR key. It can be changed by selecting the Departure box and pressing the ENTR key to display the departure list.

- Standard arrivals are added in a manner similar to that used for departures:

  1. Add the destination airport to your flight plan.

  2. Select the Arr box of the arrival airport and press the ENTR key.

  3. Select the arrival you want and press ENTR to confirm it.

  4. If necessary, select the appropriate transition and press ENTR to confirm it.

- Some standard arrivals include specific routings which depend on the landing runway in use. If you are using one of these, you must enter the arrival runway in the Rwy box on the arrival airport waypoint. The landing runway is generally not known before departure, so you must do this while you are enroute.

- **You must enter the landing runway before you program the instrument approach procedure. Failure to do so will result in arrival waypoints being missed in the flight plan.**

Headings to Intercept a Radial

- You can program the IFD to intercept any flight plan leg by using the IFD Multi-Function knob or the touch screen to select the "to" waypoint, pressing the Activate Leg line select key, and then confirming your selection by pressing the ENTR key.

- You can program the IFD to intercept a "random" radial of any waypoint by using this procedure:

  1. Use the IFD Multi-Function knob or the touch screen to select the waypoint you want to navigate to.

  2. Press the Activate Leg line select key and then confirm your selection by pressing the ENTR key.

  3. Press the OBS knob to put the IFD into OBS mode.

  4. Select your "to" radial with the OBS knob or, more likely, the course selector of your HSI or navigation indicator.

Course Offsets

- You can offset your flight plan a specified distance left or right of course by using the Offset line select key. This is done with the following procedure:

  1. Select the waypoint at the end of the current leg.

  2. Press the Offset line select key.

  3. Use the IFD Multi-Function knob to set an offset distance. Offsets right or left of course can be selected.

- An offset can be cancelled by doing the following:

  1. Select the waypoint at the end of the current leg.

  2. Press the Offset line select key.

  3. Press the Delete Offset line select key.

Changing a Flight Plan with Rubber Band Mode

- A flight plan leg can be graphically altered on the IFD screen by "rubber banding" it.

- To rubber band a leg, place your finger on it for at least two seconds. The leg will turn cyan. Then use your finger to drag it to the position where a new waypoint is to be inserted.

- If the insertion point is near an existing intersection or navaid, that fix will be added to the flight plan. Otherwise a new rubber band waypoint will be added.

- Confirm the new waypoint by pressing ENTR. Reject it by pressing CLR.

- The new waypoint will be inserted between the two waypoints which define the leg that was rubber banded.

- Use the Direct button if you want to go direct to the new waypoint.

Enroute Vertical Navigation

- All IFD models support enroute Vertical Navigation (VNAV) for descents.

- The Path Basis for enroute VNAV can be either Descent Rate or Descent Angle.

- An altitude constraint must be set into a flight plan waypoint.

- A Top of Descent (TOD) icon represents the point where the descent must begin. The display will provide a 9 second count-down timer when approaching the TOD.

- When the TOD point is reached, the timer will change to a "Begin Descent Now" advisory.

- A "Vertical Direct To" button is provided to command the descent guidance to begin.

- GPS+V will display in the upper right corner of the display indicating that you are navigating using GPS with Vertical Information.

- SVS will display an HDI and VDI for descent guidance and will also display "VNAV" above the VDI.

- A "VNAV Terminated" advisory will display on the FMS Map and SVS page (if equipped) at the bottom of the descent.

Lesson 7: Saving and Reusing Flight Plans

The previous lessons taught you how to build complicated flight plans, including standard departures, airways, and standard arrivals. Flight plans like these can get complicated; it takes a while to key in all the information. If you fly the same routes on a regular basis you might want to type in the flight plan just once, store it away, and retrieve it whenever you want it. Or, if you're planning a long trip with several stops, you might want to plan each segment ahead of time and save all the flight plans while you're preparing for the trip. Then, at each stop, you could just retrieve the relevant flight plan and be ready to go. The "saved flight plan feature" of the IFD5XX/4XX lets you do just that.

In this lesson you will learn to save a flight plan for later use, retrieve it when you need it, make copies of it, and invert it for use on your trip back home. You will also learn how to delete stored flight plans.

At the end of this lesson you will be know how to use all the capabilities of the IFD's saved flight plan feature.

The Scenario

You are back at the St. Paul Downtown Airport (KSTP), preparing for your trip to EAA AirVenture in Oshkosh (KOSH). Your family members are coming along and you want to have your airplane ready at departure time and not spend a lot of time loading flight plans while your passengers are waiting.

Oshkosh gets pretty busy during AirVenture time. You want to plan your flights to comply with the FAA's AirVenture NOTAM, and you also want to stay clear of the military airspace in the middle of Wisconsin. After looking at the NOTAM and your charts, you decide on the following routes:

> KSTP to KOSH: EAU MAXMA WLCHS RIPON

> KOSH to KSTP: CEBMU GWIZZ MAXMA EAU

The arrival route brings you in over RIPON, which is the main Oshkosh arrival gate. The departure route takes you over the preferred IFR departure gate. Both routes remain clear of the FALLS2 MOA.

Let's set this up in the IFD540 simulator. Proceed as follows:

Start the IFD540 Simulator and Build the Flight Plan on the FPL Page

As before, you will prepare for your flights by building a flight plan on the FPL page.

- ☑ Start the IFD540 simulator program on your iPad.
- ☑ Use the **FMS** rocker to display the **FPL** page.
- ☑ If necessary, open the split-screen flight plan map by tapping on the **MAP** tab on the left side of the display.
- ☑ Build the KSTP EAU MAXMA WLCHS RIPON KOSH flight plan on the **FPL** page, just as you did before. Review the previous lessons for details.
- ☑ Press the **Activate Flight Plan** line select key.

When you're finished, your IFD540 display screen should look like this:

Figure 7 - 1 The KSTP–KOSH Flight Plan

Storing a Flight Plan for Later Use

So far you've built a flight plan just like you did before. But now things will get a little different. You're not going flying right away; you want to save the flight plan for later use.

You can do this as follows:

☑ Press the right side of the **FMS** rocker twice or tap on the **ROUTE** tab to display the ROUTE page.

This is the page that is used to save and retrieve flight plans. It includes:

- **Current Route** box – This is the flight plan that's currently loaded into your **FPL** page. Note that it shows your origin and destination airports.

- **New Route** box – You can select this to build a new stored flight plan from scratch.

- **Route boxes** – A separate route box will appear for each saved route.

- **Route Management line select keys** – These are used to perform operations on the saved routes. The captions on the keys will change depending on what is being shown in the main section of the display.

Your display will have route boxes on it if flight plans have already been saved in your IFD.

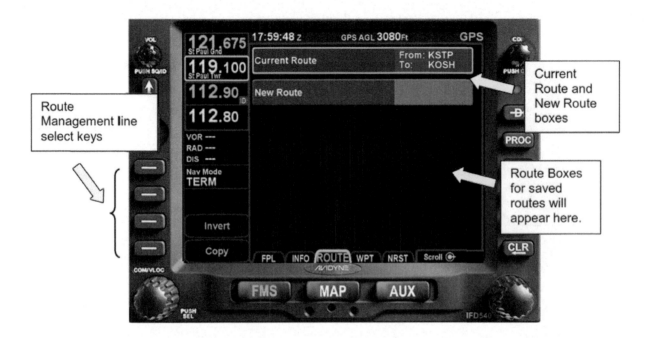

Figure 7 - 2 The ROUTE Tab

☑ The top **Current Route** box should be the selected route, indicated by the cyan edit cursor that is surrounding it. If it's not, select it by tapping on it or by turning the **IFD Multi-Function Knob**.

☑ Press the line select key next to **Copy**. This will copy the selected route to a new saved route and open the new route for editing.

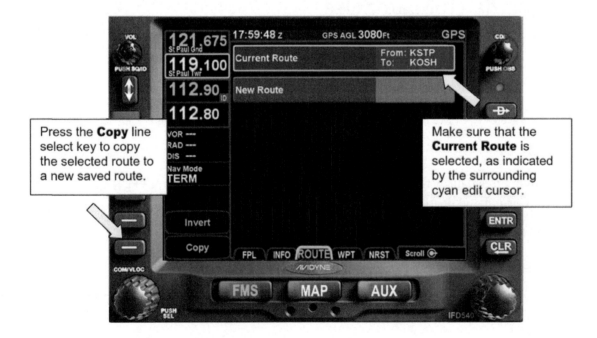

Figure 7 - 3 Copying the Current Route

The new saved route can now be edited just like the routes you worked with previously on the FMS FPL page. This route doesn't need any changes. It would, however, be useful to give it a name so you can easily recognize it in the future.

Lesson 7: Saving and Reusing Flight Plans

☑ Tap on the blue **Name** field at the top of the display. The on-screen keyboard will appear.

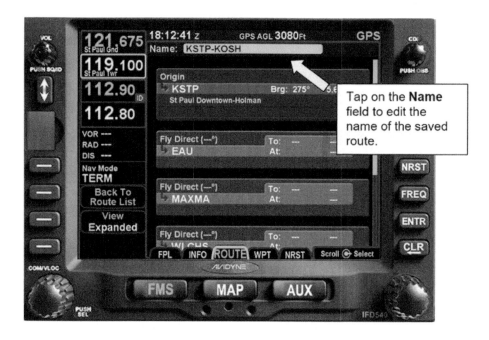

Figure 7 - 4 Selecting the Route Name Box

☑ Use the on-screen keyboard to type in the new name for this route: **OSH AIRVENTURE**. (You could also enter each letter with the **IFD Multi-Function** knob, but that would be a lot more work. You're doing this on the ground and hopefully the turbulence is minimal.)

If you make a mistake while typing, you can use the **CLR** key to erase the letter. Pressing **CLR** multiple times will erase your new name and take you back to the original name.

☑ Press the on-screen **Enter** button to accept the new name when it is complete.

Figure 7 - 5 Keying in the New Route Name

Lesson 7: Saving and Reusing Flight Plans

☑ The new route has now been renamed. Press the **Back to Route List** line select key to display the list of saved routes. You will see that your new route has been added.

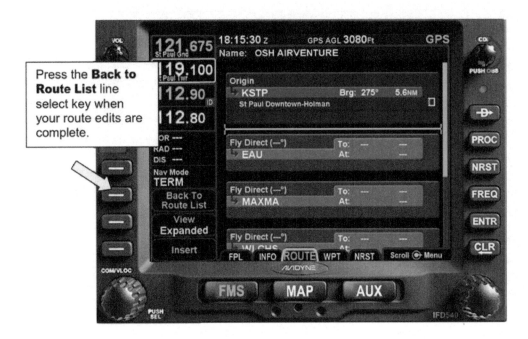

Figure 7 - 6 Going Back to the Route List

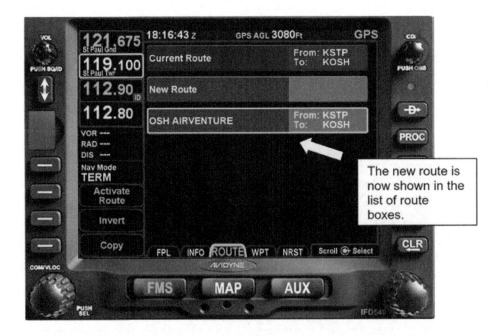

Figure 7 - 7 The Route List with the New Route Added

Inverting a Stored Flight Plan

Preparation for your trip to Oshkosh is complete, but what about the return trip? Departure from AirVenture is always a busy time. It's best to get your homeward flight plan set up now. Fortunately, this is easy. You just have to "invert" the outbound flight plan to copy it a new one in the opposite direction.

☑ With the cursor around OSH AIRVENTURE, press the **Invert** line select key.

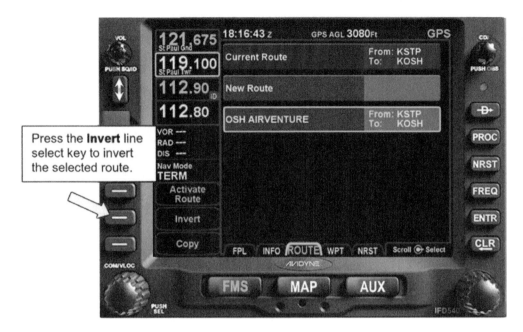

Figure 7 - 8 Using the Invert Line Select Key

When you press the **Invert** key a new route is created. It is the same as the selected route except all the waypoints are in the opposite order. The route editing page automatically appears on the screen, allowing you to edit the new route as necessary.

☑ Using the same procedure as you did before, change the name of the new route to **HOME FROM OSH**.

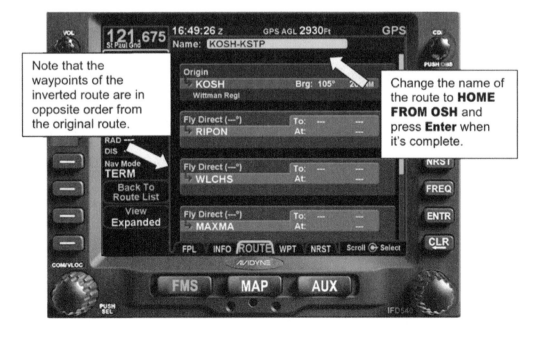

Figure 7 - 9 The Inverted Route

Lesson 7: Saving and Reusing Flight Plans

☑ Press the **Back to Route List** line select key. The **ROUTE** page now appears, showing the route you have just added.

> **Note:** The IFD displays routes sorted by origin and then by destination.

Figure 7 - 10 Route List with Both New Routes

Editing a Stored Flight Plan

As you probably noticed, the return flight from Oshkosh had a slightly different routing than the flight into Oshkosh. The return route you just created did not take this into account, so you'll have to go back and fix it. You can do this by editing your stored flight plan.

The correct routing is KOSH CEBMU GWIZZ MAXMA EAU KSTP. Update your stored flight plan as follows:

☑ Select the **HOME FROM OSH** route box by tapping on it or selecting it with the **IFD Multi-Function Knob**.

☑ Tap on the route box again or press the **ENTR** key. This will display the stored route.

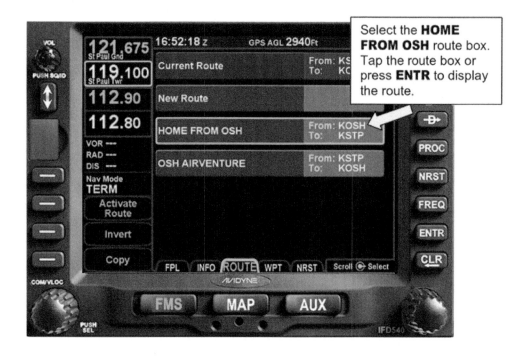

Figure 7 - 11 Selecting a Route for Editing

☑ Now you can edit the route just like you learned to do on the **FPL** page. In this case, you should:

1. Delete the **RIPON** and **WLCHS** waypoints.

2. Add the **CEBMU** and **GWIZZ** waypoints.

3. Scroll through the entire route to ensure that it is correct.

☑ Press the **Back to Route List** line select key when you are finished.

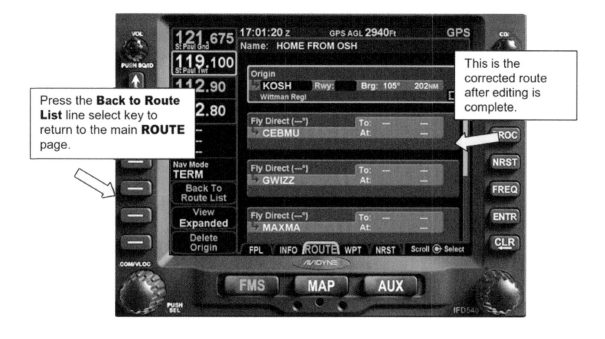

Figure 7 - 12 The Corrected Route

Creating a New Stored Flight Plan

The saved flight plans you have created so far were made by copying a current flight plan and by inverting and editing a saved flight plan. You can also create new flight plans from scratch directly on the **ROUTE** page. This is done with the New Route box.

Let's create a simple flight plan to see how this works.

☑ Tap on the **New Route** box once to select it, then once again to display the route editing page. This creates a blank new route.

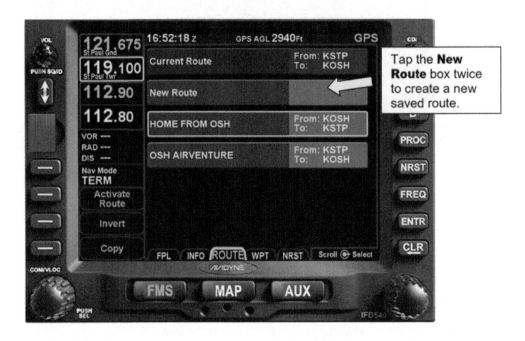

Figure 7 - 13 Creating a New Stored Route

☑ For the purpose of this exercise you will not create a name for the route; you will just use the default. Tap on the **Name** field twice to accept the default name. You can also press the **ENTR** key twice.

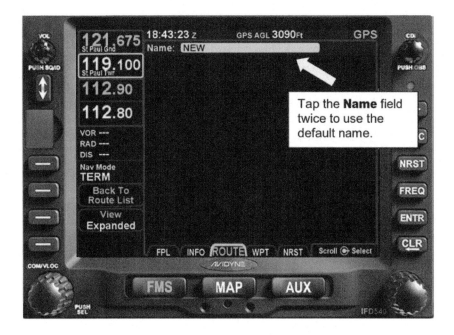

Figure 7 - 14 Using the Default Route Name

☑ An empty route page will now be displayed. Use the same procedure as before to enter the simple flight plan **KSTP KOSH**. This is the direct route between St. Paul and Oshkosh. The name of the route is automatically changed to the departure and arrival airports.

> **Note:** If you have two saved routes with the same arrival and departure points they will both have the same name. This can create confusion, possibly causing you to select the wrong route. It's better to assign a unique name to each saved route.

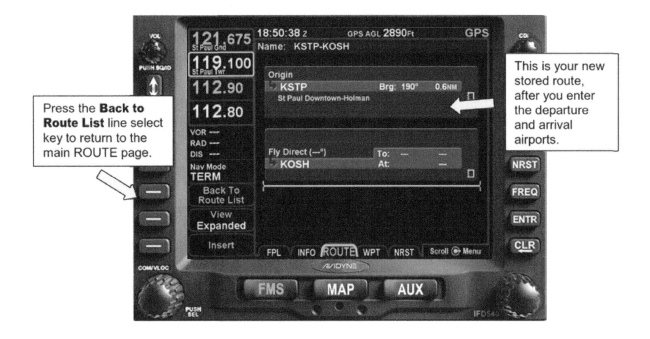

Figure 7 - 15 Entering and Saving the New Stored Route

☑ Press the **Back to Route List** line select key. The new saved route has been added to the route list.

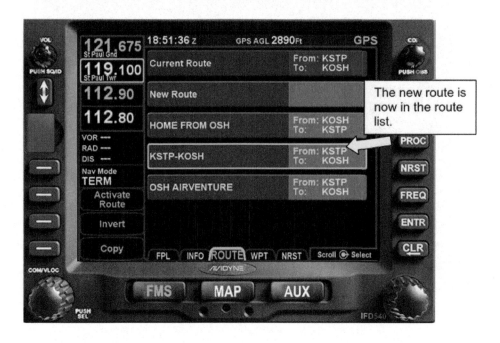

Figure 7 - 16 Route List Showing the New Stored Route

Activating a Stored Flight Plan

Now you have built several stored routes and you are ready for your Oshkosh trip. But how do you retrieve them when it's time to go flying?

Let's find out:

☑ To simulate the beginning of your trip, shut down the IFD540 simulator and start it up again. This will clear out the **FPL** page, just as the real IFD540 is when you power it up. (The active IFD flight plan is always erased when the unit is turned off.)

☑ Use the **FMS** rocker to bring up the ROUTE page.

☑ Tap on the **OSH AirVenture** route box, or use the **IFD Multi-Function** knob to select it.

☑ Press the **Activate Route** line select key.

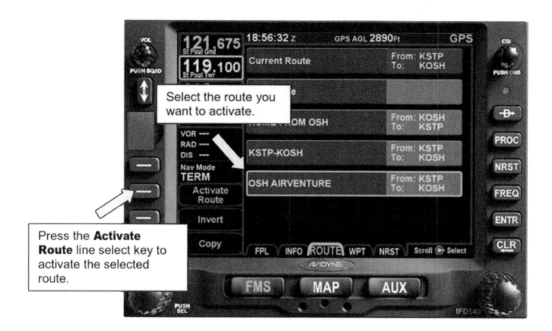

Figure 7 - 17 Activating a Stored Flight Plan

Note: If the **FPL** tab already contains an active route, an **Activate** box will be displayed when you try to replace it with a stored route. Tap on it or press the **ENTR** key to accept the activation of the new route. It will replace the previous flight plan.

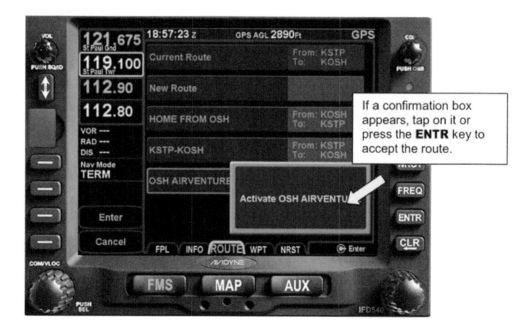

Figure 7 - 18 Confirming the Route Activation

☑ The IFD540 will now return to the **FPL** tab. The activated route appears there, showing that it is now the current route.

Lesson 7: Saving and Reusing Flight Plans

Figure 7 - 19 The Activated Route on the Flight Plan Page

Deleting a Saved Flight Plan

When your trip is over you may want to clean things up by deleting unneeded flight plans. Let's demonstrate this by deleting the direct KSTP-KOSH flight plan that you built in the previous section.

- ☑ Use the **FMS** rocker switch to return to the ROUTE tab.

- ☑ Select the **KSTP-KOSH** route box.

- ☑ Press the **CLR** key.

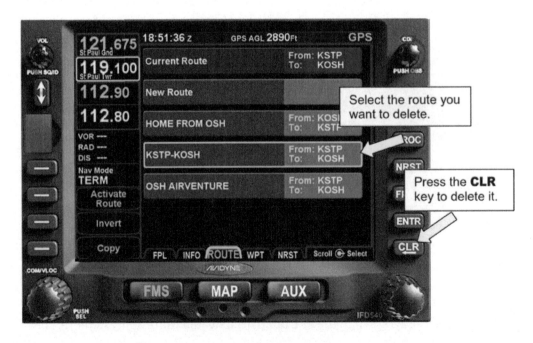

Figure 7 - 20 Deleting a Stored Route

Lesson 7: Saving and Reusing Flight Plans

☑ A box will appear asking you to confirm the deletion. Tap the box or press the **ENTR** key. The saved route is now deleted.

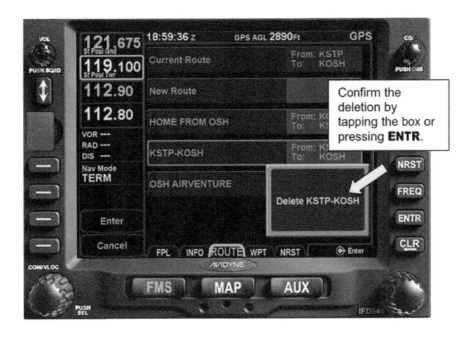

Figure 7 - 21 Confirming the Route Deletion

Deleting the Current Flight Plan

Sometimes you build a flight plan on the FMS FPL page and, for whatever reason, you want to delete the whole thing and start over again. You can do this from the **FPL** page by deleting each waypoint using the the **CLR** key, which can be tedious on a large flight plan. An easier method is to delete the whole route on the **ROUTE** page (Fig 7-21).

Remember that the current flight plan is always shown in the magenta box at the top of the **ROUTE** page. It can be deleted just like any other saved route. The only difference is that the **Current Route** box doesn't disappear. But all the waypoints in the current flight plan do.

Use the following procedure to delete the current flight plan:

☑ Use the **FMS** rocker key to display the **ROUTE** page.

☑ Select the **Current Route** box.

☑ Press the **CLR** key.

☑ Confirm the deletion by pressing the **ENTR** key.

☑ The **FPL** page is now displayed, showing an empty flight plan.

IFD440/410 Differences

All the flight planning procedures that have been explored in this lesson work exactly the same way on the IFD440 and the IFD410 as they do on the IFD550 and IFD540. The only difference is that the IFD440/410 has a much smaller screen.

Figure 7 - 22 IFD440 Route Tab

Lesson Review

This lesson taught you how to store, edit, retrieve, and delete saved flight plans. The items that were discussed are:

Saving a Flight Plan

- The IFD540 can save flight plans for later retrieval. This is useful when you fly the same route often. It saves the work of re-entering flight plan each time you want to use it.

- The current flight plan can be saved to a new stored route by using the following procedure:

  1. Go to the FMS ROUTE page.

  2. Select the Current Route from the list of route boxes.

  3. Press the Copy line select key.

- The saved flight plan can be given a name by typing in the Name box on the route editing page. It's good practice to give each saved route a unique name.

- When the saved route is complete, press the Back to Route List line select key to return to the route list display.

Inverting a Flight Plan

- It is often useful to reverse a flight plan so you can travel back over a route in the opposite direction.

- A saved flight plan can be reversed by pressing the INVERT line select key on the ROUTE page. This creates a new saved copy of the flight plan with waypoints in the opposite order of the original.

Editing a Saved Flight Plan

- A stored route can be edited by the following procedure:

    1. Select it on the ROUTE page.

    2. Press the ENTR key or tap on the route box to display the route.

    3. Make the required edits.

    4. Press the Back to Route List line select key to return to the route list display.

Creating a New Saved Flight Plan

- A new saved route can be created as follows:

    1. Tap on the New Route box on the ROUTE page.

    2. Type in a new route name, or accept the default name.

    3. Enter the waypoints of the route as you would do on the FPL page.

    4. Press the Back to Route List line select key to return to the route list display.

Activating a Saved Flight Plan

- Copying a stored route to the current flight plan page is called "activating" it.

- To activate a saved route:

    1. Select the saved route box on the ROUTE page.

    2. Press the Activate Route line select key.

    3. Accept the activation by tapping on the confirmation box.

Deleting a Saved Flight Plan

- Old flight plans should be deleted from the saved route page to avoid clutter and confusion.

- To delete a saved route:

    1. Select the route to be deleted on the ROUTE page.

    2. Press the CLR key.

    3. Accept the deletion by tapping on the confirmation box.

Deleting the Current Flight Plan

- The entire flight plan shown on the FPL page can be deleted as follows:

    1. Go to the ROUTE page.

    2. Select the Current route box.

    3. Press the CLR key.

    4. Accept the deletion by tapping on the confirmation box.

Lesson 7: Saving and Reusing Flight Plans

Lesson 8: Holding Patterns

This lesson will explore holding patterns.

Holding patterns can be complicated and are used relatively infrequently. Pilots who are not flying in congested areas may not be required to use a "real" holding pattern for years on end. But when ATC tells you to hold, it's very important that you get it right. There's a reason for a hold, usually nearby traffic or nearby terrain. Wandering outside the limits of the holding airspace can have severe consequences. Fortunately, the IFD5XX/4XX can help you.

Holds are used to park you in a specified spot in the sky when the airspace ahead is congested. They can also be used to perform course reversals in some instrument approaches and they provide a place for you to go after missing an approach. Holds can be published or they can be random. Published holds appear on charts and procedures. Random holds are assigned by ATC on-the-fly as needed.

This lesson will focus on "parking" holds, used by ATC to prevent you from entering airspace that doesn't have room for you. Holds associated with instrument approach procedures will be explored in the next lesson. Everything that you learn in this chapter can also be used in the approach holding patterns that will come later.

The Avidyne IFD navigators are fully capable of flying any holding pattern, random or published, that ATC throws at you. Once programmed correctly, the IFDXX/4XX will automatically show you how to enter, execute, and exit any holding pattern. If coupled to your autopilot, they will fly the hold for you with very little input from the pilot. All this sounds easy, and it can be. But it's extremely important for you to be completely familiar with using your Avidyne navigator for holding. Holds can be issued with little warning and little time to prepare. It's up to you to maintain your proficiency so you won't be caught by surprise.

At the end of this lesson you will know how to program any holding pattern into your IFD navigator. You'll know how the navigator will fly the hold and be familiar with its indications as it does so. You'll be ready to start learning about instrument approaches in the next lesson.

The IFD's Holding Ability

The IFD5XX/4XX navigators are capable of performing a holding pattern at any waypoint that is defined as a specific point in space. That includes all the types of waypoints we have seen so far: named intersections, navigation facilities, and airports. It will also hold at user-defined waypoints. There are other types of waypoints, such as altitude crossing points that do not support a hold.

A hold can be inserted into a flight plan just as you would insert a waypoint. The hold is placed after the waypoint which defines the holding fix.

The IFD gives you complete flexibility in constructing a hold. You can specify the holding radial, the direction of turn, and the length of the holding leg. You are not restricted by the hold parameters published on your charts.

Let's set up a scenario to see how all this works.

The Scenario

This scenario will begin at the airport in Moline, IL (KMLI). You are flying a trip to Chicago Midway (KMDW). Your planned route is:

KMLI JPAUL V156 BDF BDF.MOTIF6 KMDW

Your weather briefing shows a forecast for thunderstorms and you know that Midway is always busy with airline traffic. There's a good chance of holding if a storm cell moves over the airport or one of its arrival gates.

Let's set this up in the IFD540 simulator. Proceed as follows:

Start the IFD540 Simulator and Build the Flight Plan on the FPL Page

As before, you will prepare for your flights by building a flight plan on the **FPL** page.

- ☑ Start the IFD540 simulator program on your iPad.
- ☑ Use the **FMS** rocker to display the **FPL** page.
- ☑ If necessary, open the split-screen flight plan map by tapping on the **MAP** tab on the left side of the display.
- ☑ Build the **KMLI JPAUL V156 BDF BDF.MOTIF6 KMDW** flight plan on the **FPL** page, using the procedures you've learned already. Review the previous lessons if necessary.
- ☑ Check the entire flight plan to make sure it has been entered correctly.
- ☑ Press the **Activate Flight Plan** line select key.

When you're finished, your IFD540 display screen should look like this:

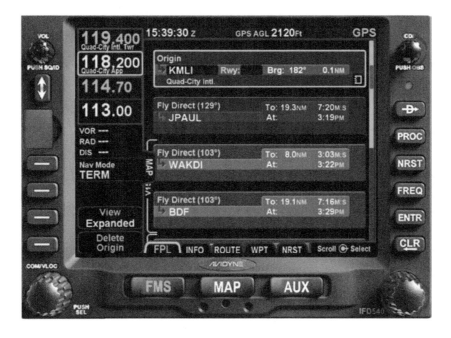

Figure 8 - 1 The KMLI – KMDW Flight Plan

After the flight plan has been built you are ready to go flying. Continue the scenario:

☑ Press the **MAP** rocker under the display screen. This will display the **MAP** page so you can watch your flight.

☑ Let the airplane proceed until you are established on course. If necessary, press the **IFD Multi-Function Knob** to put the map in track-up orientation.

Building and Flying a "Random" Hold

Programming the Hold in Your Flight Plan

Soon after departure you notice that your IFD's ADS-B weather display is showing a line of storms moving into the Chicago area. The chatter on the radio indicates that Midway has closed off arrivals and the airplanes ahead of you are starting to get holding instructions. Soon you get your own holding clearance:

"Cessna 1291S, hold south of the WAKDI intersection on the 180 degree radial, left hand turns, expect further clearance at 1615Z."

This is what we have informally defined as a "random" hold, a hold that is not published on the chart but is arbitrarily defined by ATC so as to keep you in the proper airspace. Fortunately, it's easy to program such a hold into your new IFD. Proceed as follows:

☑ Use the **FPL** rocker to display the **FPL** tab.

☑ Use the touch screen or the **IFD Multi-Function** knob to place the cursor underneath the WAKDI intersection. This is the place where you want to insert a holding pattern into your flight plan.

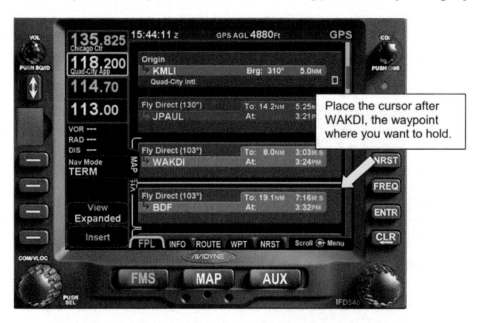

Figure 8 - 2 The Insertion Point for the Holding Pattern

☑ Press the **ENTR** key. The waypoint insertion pop-up box will appear.

☑ Use the touch screen or the **IFD Multi-Function** knob to select **HOLD AT WAKDI**.

☑ Now press the **ENTR** key again to accept the hold.

Lesson 8: Holding Patterns

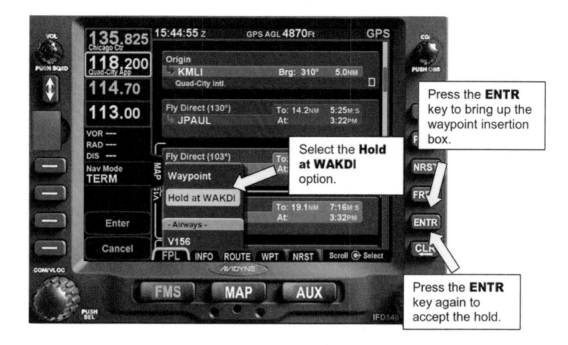

Figure 8 - 3 Inserting the Hold into the Flight Plan

A new hold has been inserted in your flight plan after the WAKDI intersection. Close inspection, however, will show that it is not the hold you want. The controller told you to hold south on the 180 degree radial using left hand turns. This holding pattern is west of WAKDI on the 283 degree radial using right hand turns.

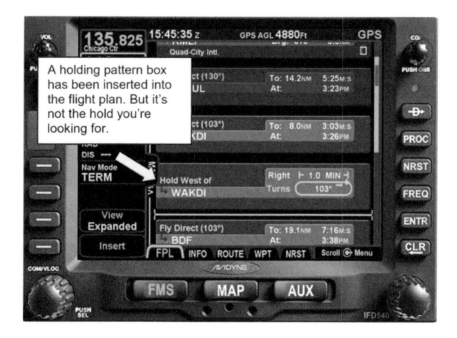

Figure 8 - 4 The New Hold, Before Modification

Why did this happen? It happened because there was no published hold at WAKDI. Since nothing was published the IFD assumed that you would want a standard right turn holding pattern along the radial that defines the airway. You can see this by tapping on the **MAP** tab, moving the cursor to the new holding pattern, and using the **View Cursor** feature to look at your flight plan. You can see that the new hold is directly along your flight plan and uses right hand turns.

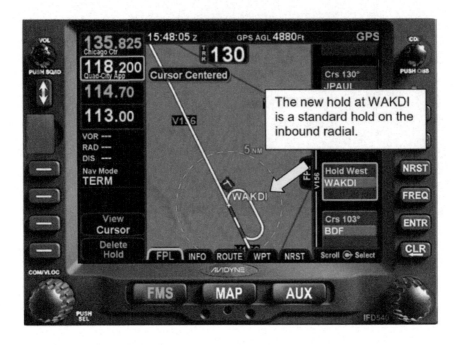

Figure 8 - 5 The Standard Hold at WAKDI Intersection

Unfortunately, this is not the hold that you were issued. Let's fix it.

☑ Tap the vertical **FPL** tab next to the flight plan waypoints to close the flight plan map. You have to do this because the details of the hold won't be displayed when the map is open.

☑ Turn the inner **IFD Multi-Function** knob to select the **RIGHT** field. The field will turn cyan. This entry indicates whether the hold is to the right or to the left.

☑ Press the **ENTR** key once. The **RIGHT** field will turn white.

☑ Turn the **IFD Multi-Function** knob. As you do so, the field will alternate between **RIGHT** and **LEFT**. Stop when it is showing **LEFT**.

☑ Press the **ENTR** key again to accept the new value.

Note: If you would rather use the touch screen, you can simply tap on the **RIGHT** field. Each time you tap it will alternate between **RIGHT** and **LEFT**. There is no need to press the **ENTR** key.

Note: As you alternate between **RIGHT** and **LEFT** the small arrow on the holding pattern graphic will go up and down to indicate the direction of the turn.

Lesson 8: Holding Patterns

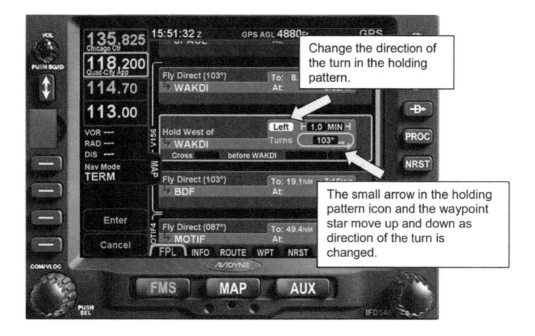

Figure 8 - 6 Modifying the Holding Pattern

The direction of the hold has been set. Now you have to enter the holding radial. ATC issues hold instructions using *radials*, However, when programming a hold into the IFD, you must specify the inbound *course*, not the radial. Therefore, you must always remember the following:

When ATC issues a holding radial, you must always enter the opposite (reciprocal) course into the IFD holding box. The reciprocal course is computed by adding or subtracting 180 degrees from the holding radial.

In the case of the holding clearance you have been issued, ATC told you to hold on the 180 degree radial. Therefore, you must enter the reciprocal inbound course, 360, into the IFD.

- ☑ Use the **IFD Multi-Function** knob to select the **103** field in the holding pattern flight plan block.

- ☑ Press the **ENTR** key.

- ☑ Use the **IFD Multi-Function** knob to change the entry to **360**. The inner knob controls the "ones" digits, while the outer knob controls the "tens."

- ☑ Press the **ENTR** key again to accept the new holding course.

> Note: If you would rather use the touch screen, tap on the 103 field to select it, then tap it again to display the on-screen keyboard. Type in the holding course and then press the **Enter** button or the **ENTR** key.

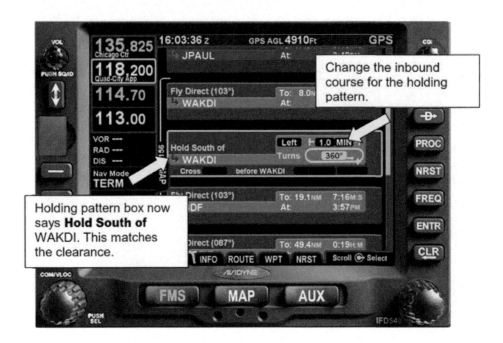

Figure 8 - 7 The Updated Holding Pattern

When the holding course has been entered the direction field on the flight plan holding box is automatically changed. It now says **Hold South of**, instead of **Hold West of**. This complies with the holding clearance you were given.

You can see your completed holding pattern by tapping the vertical **MAP** tab and using the **View Cursor** function to inspect your flight plan. You can see that the holding pattern is now oriented properly, with turns in the correct direction.

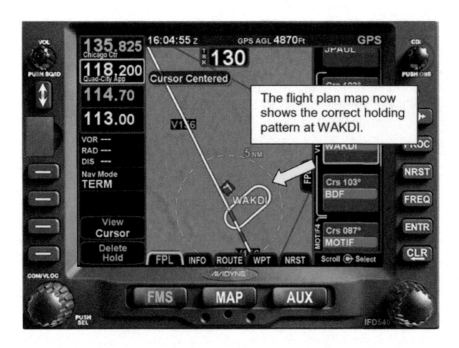

Figure 8 - 8 Map View of the Updated Holding Pattern

> **Note:** If you want to delete a hold before you reach it, use the same procedure you would use to delete a waypoint: Place the cursor on the holding flight plan box and then press the **CLR** key. Alternately, you can press the **Delete Hold** line select key.
>
> This should not be done after the hold has been entered. Once you are in a hold you should use one of the exit procedures which will be discussed below.

Entering and Flying the Hold

As your simulated flight continues you will soon approach the holding fix. Let's look at the IFD MAP page to see how it tells you what's going to happen when you get to the holding waypoint.

Press the **MAP** rocker to display the **MAP** tab.

Note the following indications:

- The flight plan leg that you are currently flying is displayed in magenta.

- The first part of the holding pattern entry is displayed as a magenta barber pole. This is the next leg that you will be flying.

- The rest of the holding pattern and the leg beyond the holding fix is displayed in white.

- The display tells you that your aircraft is going to enter the hold using a parallel entry. The leg beyond the holding fix is white, showing that it is not the next leg and it will not be flown until the hold is completed.

Figure 8 - 9 Holding Pattern Components

As you cross the holding fix a message will appear telling you that the IFD is performing a parallel entry.

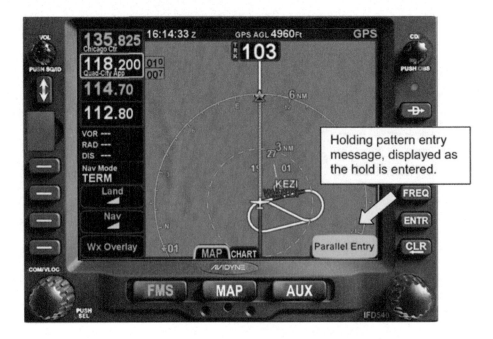

Figure 8 - 10 Holding Pattern Entry Message

The aircraft will turn to enter the hold. As it performs the entry the legs will change colors, always showing the current leg in magenta and the next leg as a barber pole.

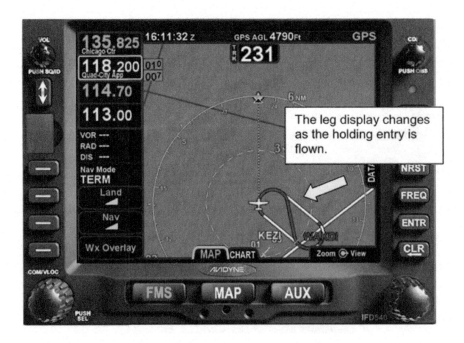

Figure 8 - 11 Entering the Holding Pattern

When you are fully established the entire hold will be displayed in magenta. All other legs will be white. There are no barber-pole legs, indicating that there is no "next" leg.

Your aircraft will remain in the hold indefinitely until you do something to initiate an exit.

Lesson 8: Holding Patterns

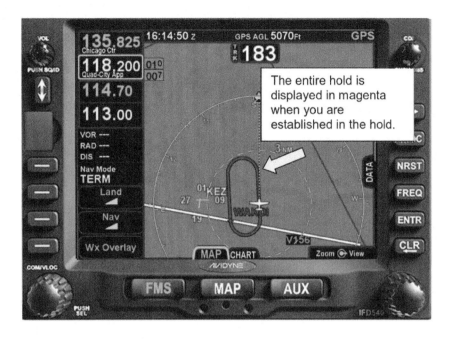

The entire hold is displayed in magenta when you are established in the hold.

Figure 8 - 12 Established in the Hold

Exiting the Hold

After a flying the holding pattern for a short while, you receive a new clearance:

"Cessna 1291S, after WAKDI cleared on course."

Do the following:

☑ Press the **FMS** rocker to display the **FPL** tab.

☑ Press the **Exit Hold** line select key.

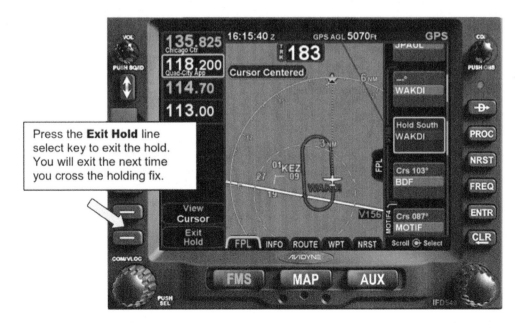

Press the **Exit Hold** line select key to exit the hold. You will exit the next time you cross the holding fix.

Figure 8 - 13 Exiting the Hold

As soon as you press the Exit Hold key, a message will appear that says **Exiting Hold at Fix**. This indicates that the IFD will continue the holding pattern until the aircraft crosses the holding fix. Then it will exit the hold and fly the next leg of the flight plan.

You can confirm this by observing the colors of the flight plan legs. The holding pattern is still shown in magenta, but the leg past the holding fix is now displayed as a barber pole, indicating that it is now the next leg.

Figure 8 - 14 Holding Pattern Exit Process

When the aircraft reaches the WAKDI intersection it will exit the hold and proceed with the rest of the flight plan.

Figure 8 - 15 After the Holding Pattern Has Been Exited

Programming a Published Hold

Unlike the "random" hold you just performed, most holds are published on your charts. Having a published hold makes the ATC controller's work easier by reducing communications and misunderstandings. It also makes your work easier, as we'll soon see.

A good example of a published hold is the holding pattern shown at the BFD VOR in the MOTIF6 arrival, shown below. The hold is southwest of BDF on the 247 degree radial, with right-hand turns. This same hold is also depicted on the printed low altitude enroute chart.

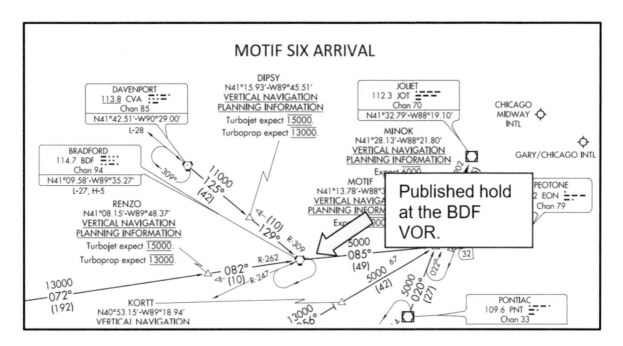

Figure 8 - 16 Published Hold at BDF in MOTIF6 Arrival

Published holding patterns are included in the IFD's internal database, so the IFD should know the proper procedure when you set up a holding pattern at a published waypoint. Even though this is usually the case, there are exceptions.

It is always your responsibility as pilot-in-command to make sure that the holding pattern you program into the IFD is the same as the one published on your charts. Always check the holding pattern parameters to ensure that they are correct.

Let's continue the scenario to demonstrate the use of a published hold.

As your flight continues past the WAKDI intersection you soon receive yet another holding clearance:

> *"Cessna 1291S, hold as published at Bradford, five mile legs, expect further clearance at 1700Z."*

This clearance tells you to hold at the BDF waypoint as shown on the MOTIF6 arrival chart. It does have one difference, though. The clearance is for five mile holding legs, rather than the usual one minute legs. The controller is trying to reduce your workload by letting you fly longer holding legs, thus lowering the number of turns you have to make.

Take the following steps to set up this hold in the IFD:

☑ Press the **FMS** rocker to display the **FPL** tab.

☑ Place the cursor under the **BDF** waypoint. This is where you want to insert the new holding pattern.

☑ Press the **ENTR** key. A selection box will pop up. Select **Hold at BDF**.

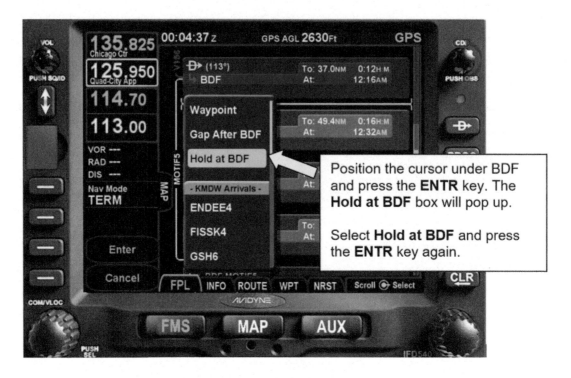

Figure 8 - 17 Programming the Hold at BDF

☑ Press the **ENTR** key again. Another selection box will appear, asking you which holding pattern you would like.

☑ Select **Southwest (1.0 MIN)** and press the **ENTR** key.

> **Note:** The second holding pattern selection screen appears because there can be multiple published holds at a single fix. These holds are shown on different charts (high altitude, low altitude, approach, etc.). Be sure that you are selecting the correct published hold.

The new holding pattern box now appears in your flight plan. It is positioned after the BDF waypoint.

Look at the parameters of the holding pattern. You will see that:

• The hold will be flown on the 067 degree inbound course. This is the reciprocal of the 247 degree radial from BDF, which is the radial depicted for the hold on the MOTIF6 arrival chart.

• The hold will be flown with right hand turns, as depicted on the chart.

• The hold will be flown with one minute legs. This is not the same as the clearance, so you will have to fix it.

Lesson 8: Holding Patterns

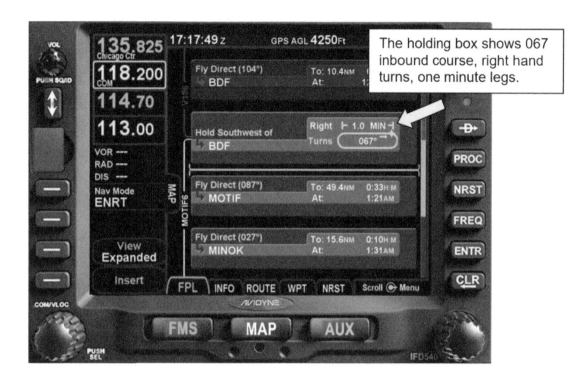

Figure 8 - 18 BDF Hold Before Modification

Do the following:

☑ Use the inner **IFD Multi-Function** knob to select the **1.0** distance field on the holding pattern block. The field color will change to cyan.

☑ Press the **ENTR** key. The field will turn white.

☑ Use the **IFD Multi-Function** knob to change the field's value to **5.0.** The inner ring controls tenths, while the outer ring controls whole numbers.

☑ Press the **ENTR** key to accept the new value.

☑ Use the same procedure to change the **MIN** field to **NM** (nautical miles).

As before, you can use the touch screen to perform the same functions. Tap on each field to select it, then tap again to display the on-screen keyboard or alternate the field's value.

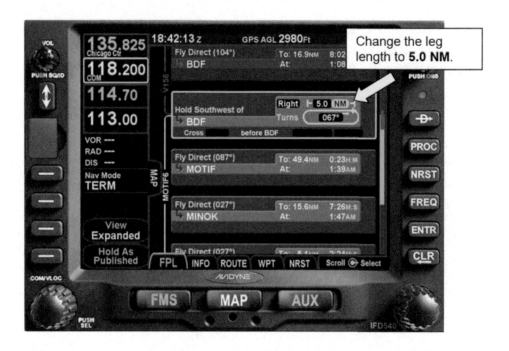

Figure 8 - 19 BDF Hold Changed to Five Mile Legs

When you have finished changing the leg length fields, inspect the holding pattern entry carefully to make sure that everything is correct. Then use the **Cursor Centered** view to look at the hold on a map. Make sure that it is oriented correctly.

This time you will use a direct holding pattern entry, so the initial turn is shown with the barber pole. The hold is elongated, indicating that it will be flown with five mile legs.

Figure 8 - 20 Map View of BDF Hold

Exiting a Holding Pattern

In the previous part of this scenario, when you held at the WAKDI intersection the hold was terminated when the ATC controller cleared you to exit the hold the next time you crossed the holding fix. Depending on where you are located in the holding pattern, this clearance may have caused you to fly a full outbound leg followed by a full inbound leg before you could exit. This could take up to four minutes to complete.

The example demonstrated a legitimate way to exit a hold, but there are other methods that take less flight time. Depending on the situation, a controller may ask you to:

- Exit the hold when you cross the holding fix, as was done in the first scenario.

- Proceed directly to another waypoint further in your flight plan.

- Proceed directly to the holding fix and then exit the hold.

The first two of these methods are straightforward. We have already seen how to tell the IFD to exit a hold, and the use of the **Direct** function was explained in a previous lesson. The third method, however, is a little tricky. It's also a very common clearance, so it's a good idea to be very familiar with it.

Continuing with the scenario we are using, you are now holding at the BDF waypoint. You receive the following clearance:

"Cessna 1291S, cleared direct to Bradford, cleared on course."

Perform the following steps:

☑ To set up the simulation, wait until the simulated aircraft has crossed the holding fix and is proceeding outbound, as shown in the figure below.

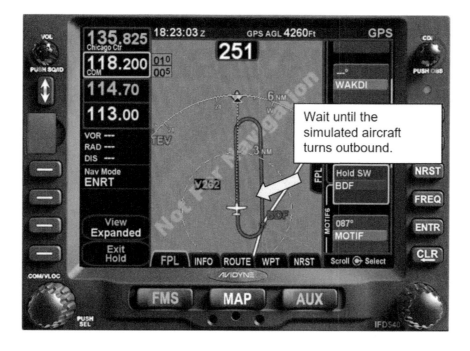

Figure 8 - 21 Aircraft in Position For Exit of BDF Hold

☑ Proceed directly to BDF by placing the cursor on the BDF waypoint and pressing the **Direct** key.

☑ Confirm by pressing the **ENTR** key twice. The aircraft will turn direct to BDF.

> **Note:** Be sure that you are going direct to the BDF waypoint, NOT the BDF holding box, located after the BDF waypoint. If you set up the flight plan to go direct to the holding box the IFD will simply re-enter the hold. That's not what you want to do.

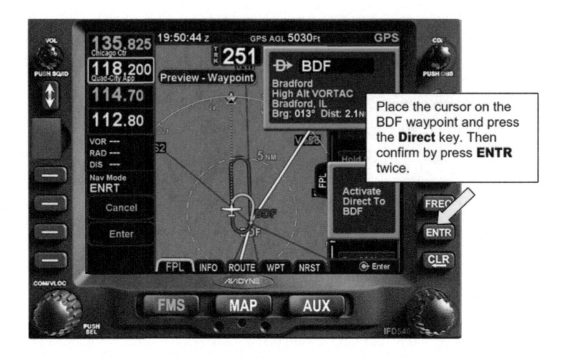

Figure 8 - 22 Exit Step 1: Go Direct to BDF

After you program the IFD to go direct to the BDF waypoint, the screen will look as it shown below and the aircraft will start a turn direct to BDF. But you're not finished. The display clearly shows that the holding pattern is still there, located after BDF. The barber pole leg shows that the first part of the hold is your next leg. The aircraft will enter the hold again if you don't do something.

These steps will finish your exit from the hold:

☑ Use the cursor to select the holding pattern flight plan box, as shown below.

☑ Press the **CLR** key to delete the hold. Or you can press the **Delete Hold** line select key.

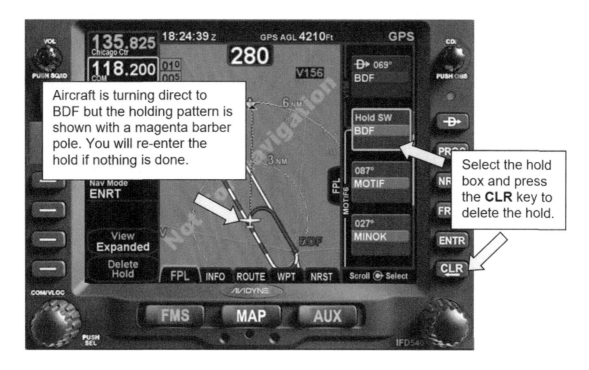

Figure 8 - 23 Exit Step 2: Delete the Hold

The hold has now been deleted. The aircraft will turn to cross the BDF waypoint, then proceed on course through the rest of the flight plan.

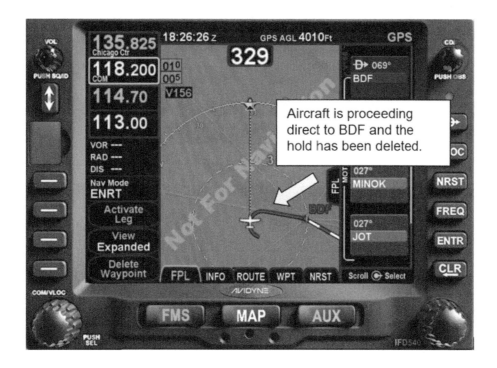

Figure 8 - 24 Updated Flight Plan After Hold is Deleted

IFD440/410 Differences

All the flight planning procedures that have been explored in this lesson work exactly the same way on the IFD440 and IFD410 as they do on the IFD550 and IFD540. The only difference is that the IFD440/410 has a much smaller screen.

Figure 8 - 25 IFD440 Holding Pattern Display

Lesson Review

This lesson taught you how to program holding patterns into an IFD5XX/4XX flight plan. You also learned how to enter, fly, and exit the hold. The items that were discussed are:

Adding a Holding Pattern to Your Flight Plan

- A holding pattern can be placed on any waypoint that is defined as a point in space.

- The IFD5XX/4XX has complete flexibility with respect to holding patterns. You can control the holding radial, the direction of turn, and the length of the holding leg.

- If a holding pattern is published on a chart, the IFD5XX/4XX will normally use it.

- If there are multiple holds associated with the same fix, the IFD will ask you to select the one you want.

- If there is no holding pattern published at the holding fix, the IFD will automatically build a standard hold along the current route of flight.

- Whether a hold is published or not, it is the responsibility of the PIC to review the programmed hold carefully to ensure that it complies with the clearance that was issued.

- ATC holding clearances usually specify the holding *radial*. The IFD uses the inbound holding *course* to specify the hold. The inbound course is the reciprocal of the radial, computed by adding or subtracting 180 degrees.

- The following procedure is used to add a hold to a flight plan:

  1. Use the FMS rocker to display the FPL tab.

  2. Position the cursor directly after the holding waypoint.

3. Press the ENTR key and select the Hold at xxxx option.

4. If multiple published holds are presented, select the one you want.

5. Press the ENTR key again to accept the hold.

6. Look at the holding pattern parameters to make sure they are what you want. If necessary, use the touch screen or the IFD Multi-Function knob to change the holding course, the turn direction, and the leg length of the hold.

7. If several holds are published at a fix, you will be asked to select the one you want. Be sure you pick the right one!

Deleting a Hold

- A hold can be deleted before you enter it by placing the cursor on the hold flight plan box and pressing the CLR key or the Delete Hold line select key.

- Once you enter a hold you should delete it by using one of the exit procedures discussed below.

Entering and Flying a Holding Pattern

- Once programmed, the IFD will automatically compute the correct holding pattern entry.

- The IFD will execute the entry and fly the hold if the navigator is coupled to an autopilot. No pilot intervention is necessary.

- It is important to watch the display of the holding pattern legs so you are always aware of what the aircraft will do next. The current leg is always colored magenta, while the next leg is a magenta barber pole. Legs beyond the next leg are white. Always make sure that the next leg is what you expect it to be.

Exiting a Holding Pattern

- There are several ways to exit a holding pattern. Which one you use will depend on the ATC clearance you receive.

- The easiest way to exit a hold is to simply go directly to another waypoint in your flight plan. This is done by selecting the fix and pressing the Direct key.

- You can exit by using the Exit Hold function of the IFD5XX/4XX. This method will cause the aircraft to finish the current circuit of the holding pattern and exit when it crosses the holding fix. To exit a hold in this manner, take the following steps:

  1. Use the FMS rocker to display the FPL tab.

  2. Press the Exit Hold line select key.

- ATC will often ask you to turn directly to the holding fix and then exit the hold. To do this:

  1. Place the cursor on the holding fix, which is the fix before the holding pattern box, and use the Direct-ENTR-ENTR key sequence to go direct to it.

  2. Place the cursor on the holding pattern flight plan box.

  3. Press CLR or the Delete Hold line select key to delete the hold.

Lesson 8: Holding Patterns

Lesson 9: Instrument & Visual Approaches

In the previous lessons you have become familiar with using VHF and GPS navigation, setting up and flying complex flight plans, and executing holding patterns with your IFD. Now it's time to put everything together and use the IFD to fly instrument approaches. This chapter will also cover the IFD's new Visual Approach capability.

This lesson will explore a variety of approach procedures, from simple to complex. You will learn about GPS, VOR, and ILS approaches, procedure turns, course reversal holds, vectors to final, and missed approaches. You will also learn how to include an alternate airport in your flight plan.

After completing this lesson you will be comfortable with the concepts of using the IFDs for instrument approaches and will be ready to practice them in your own airplane.

> **CAUTION:** This lesson uses Avidyne's IFD540 simulator to demonstrate instrument approach procedures. However, the simulator has many limitations. It cannot substitute for real world experience. You should spend a significant amount of time practicing IFD approaches in a real airplane in VFR conditions with a safety pilot before you attempt to fly them in actual IMC conditions.

Introduction

The IFD5XX and IFD4XX are fully capable VHF and GPS WAAS navigators. They can be used to shoot almost all modern instrument approach procedures. This lesson will attempt to demonstrate the most common ones, using the IFD540 simulator. However, your experience in your own aircraft will be different from the scenarios that will be explored here.

Avidyne's simulator is a good trainer for approach procedures but it does not simulate every aspect of an instrument approach. In particular:

- The simulator does not include a navigation indicator so you can't see what your CDI or HSI will do on an instrument approach.

- The simulator does not simulate a VOR or Localizer receiver. This means that it does not simulate the very important transition between GPS and VHF navigation during the last stages of a VOR or ILS approach. You'll have to see this in a real aircraft to experience how it works.

- The simulator does not simulate a glide slope. You will not be able to see how the aircraft descends on an ILS or LPV approach.

- The simulator does not simulate the interface between your IFD and the autopilot, if installed in your aircraft. Autopilots are most useful when they are used to shoot coupled instrument approaches. The exact procedure you use will always depend on the type of autopilot installed and how it is connected to the navigation system. Refer to your own manuals for details, and practice the procedures thoroughly before flying in actual IMC conditions.

With all that being said, the Avidyne IFD540 simulator is a very good tool to learn how the navigators work in a structured training environment. By practicing the scenarios below you will become comfortable with the IFDXX /4XX's instrument approach procedures and indications. Your practice approaches in an actual aircraft will be much more productive than they would be if you did not prepare with the simulator.

Lesson 9: Instrument & Visual Approaches

IFD5XX/4XX Approach Capabilities

Traditional VHF Approaches

The IFD550, IFD540, and IFD440 incorporate VHF navigation receivers and can fly traditional VHF-based approaches. These include:

- ILS approaches

- Localizer approaches

- Localizer backcourse approaches

- VOR approaches

The IFDs do not include DME receivers. However, GPS position information can be substituted for DME in most cases. Refer to the AIM for details.

The IFD545, IFD510, and IFD410 do not have VHF receivers. They can only be used for GPS approaches.

GPS Navigation: What is WAAS?

All IFD navigators have full GPS WAAS capabilities when they are installed with the proper antennas. What does that mean? It means that the IFD5XX/4XX is capable of using the enhanced GPS accuracy provided by the Wide Area Augmentation System, popularly known as WAAS.

WAAS is more generally referred to as a Satellite Based Augmentation System (SBAS). It is used in the continental United States and Alaska. Other SBAS systems are used in other parts of the world.

A WAAS-enhanced GPS receiver such as the IFD works by listening to two navigational sources at the same time. The first source is the traditional GPS satellite network, which provides a position measurement that has an accuracy of about 100 meters. The second is an error correction signal, broadcast by a different set of satellites, which improves the position accuracy to better than eight meters (usually much better).

WAAS provides the accuracy required to fly very accurate instrument approaches including those with ILS-like precision. It also includes the ability to continuously monitor its accuracy. Your IFD will know immediately if it has lost WAAS ability and it will not allow you to continue the approach. WAAS receivers do not require the RAIM checks needed by earlier GPS systems.

The IFD will normally perform WAAS navigation without any action by the pilot. You can see if WAAS is being used by using the **AUX** rocker to look at the **SYS** tab, then selecting the **GPS** page. That page will normally show **SBAS Nav** status, which indicates that you have WAAS. See the figure below.

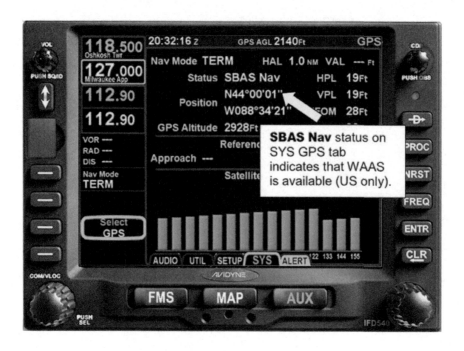

Figure 9 - 1 GPS Status Display

RNAV GPS Approaches

There are several kinds of GPS approaches, differentiated by the level of accuracy provided for guidance. It is important that you know what kind of approach you are using because it will affect the approach minimums.

The IFD will display the type of approach being used. You should use this information to select the appropriate minimums from the minimums table on the approach plate. The types of GPS approaches supported by the IFD are:

- Non-WAAS Approaches

  - LNAV (Lateral Navigation) Approaches – These are similar to non-precision approaches in that the GPS navigator provides lateral (horizontal) guidance only.

- WAAS Approaches

  - LNAV+V (Lateral Navigation with Vertical Information) Approaches – These are non-precision approaches, but the GPS navigator provides "advisory" vertical guidance on the aircraft's glide slope indicator. The glide slope can be thought of as a straight line drawn between the altitude at the final approach fix and that at the missed approach point. The glide slope does **not** consider step down fixes; they must be observed manually by the pilot. It will, however, provide you with a stabilized approach path to the MDA.

  - LNAV/VNAV (Lateral Navigation with Vertical Navigation) Approaches – This type of approach is more precise than an LNAV+V approach. It provides a glide path that is protected from obstructions but the pilot still must observe step down limitations. This type of approach is flown to a DA/DH, like an ILS, not an MDA.

  - LPV (Localizer Precision with Vertical Guidance) Approaches – This type of approach provides significantly more precision than LNAV and includes both lateral and vertical guidance. It is flown like an ILS, often to ILS-like minimums. It uses a DA/DH as its missed approach point, just like an ILS.

- LP (Localizer Performance) Approaches – These are non-precision approaches similar to localizer-only approaches. They have the precision of a localizer but no vertical guidance. They are flown to a MDA, not a DA/DH.

- LP+V (Localizer Performance with Vertical Information) Approaches – These are non-precision approaches which have localizer precision and advisory vertical guidance. The vertical guidance provides a stabilized glide slope to the MDA but does not consider any step down limitations. They are flown using the LP MDA minimums published on the approach chart. The pilot must comply with all step down fixes.

Navigation Source State Indications

With all those different types of GPS approaches, how do you know which one you are using? You get that information from two places: The approach plate minimums box shows you the basic type of approach you are flying and the IFD shows the type of navigation accuracy being used.

For example, consider the approach plate shown below. This is an RNAV GPS approach, as shown in the label in the lower right corner. However, it's not enough to know it's a GPS-based approach. You must also know what the approach minimums are. The minimums block shows that this is an LNAV approach, which means that it is to be flown as a non-precision approach. No lower minimums are provided.

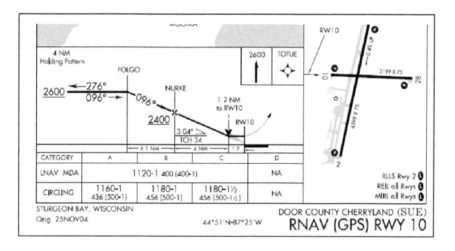

Figure 9 - 2 GPS Approach with LNAV Minimums

Another approach plate is shown below. This is also an RNAV GPS approach, but it provides several different values for minimums. The one you use will depend on the navigation capability of your aircraft.

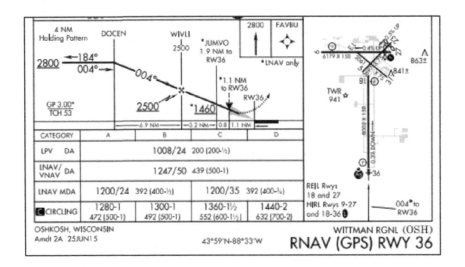

Figure 9 - 3 GPS Approach with VNAV Minimums

Therefore, you must always know what kind of guidance your IFD is giving you while you are flying an approach. This information is obtained from the display of the IFD, where the type of navigation being used is shown in the **Navigation Source State** box in the display's upper right corner. In this case, the source state is **LNAV+V**, as shown below.

Figure 9 - 4 IFD540 Showing LNAV+V Approach

As described in the previous section, LNAV+V means that the IFD navigator is giving you a glide slope indication, but the glide slope is only "advisory" and does not protect you from step down limitations on the approach. On this approach there is a limitation at the NURKE intersection, which must not be crossed lower than 2400 feet. The glide slope given by the IFD will not necessarily keep you above that altitude; you are responsible for making sure that you are not too low when you cross the fix.

Lesson 9: Instrument & Visual Approaches

As you can see, it is extremely important to know your navigation source state so you can use the correct minimums for your approach. The possible source states are:

- VLOC: VHF VOR or localizer navigation

- GPS: GPS navigation. This will be replaced by a more specific approach state when the approach begins.

- OBS: Course has been selected by the pilot using the CDI knob on the nav indicator.

- LPV, LNAV, LNAV+V, etc.: Specific approach mode, as described above.

In addition, the IFD also displays "transition" navigation source state modes. These are shown when the navigator is currently in one mode but will soon transition to another as the approach begins. The navigation source state box will show both states, separated by a horizontal arrow pointing from the current to the future state. The transition modes are:

- GPS →VLOC: Currently navigating with GPS, VLOC state is armed for VOR, localizer or ILS approach.

- GPS →LPV, LNAV, LNAV+V, etc.: Currently navigating with GPS, armed for GPS approach.

- OBS →VLOC: Currently navigating on manually selected OBS course, VLOC state is armed for VOR, localizer, or ILS approach.

Navigation Mode and CDI Scaling

In addition to the navigation source state, a pilot should be aware of the **Navigation Mode** which is being used. Navigation Mode refers to the level of navigation accuracy in effect and, in particular, the associated scaling of the CDI. The IFD automatically changes navigation mode as you depart your origin airport, fly enroute, and arrive at your destination. The level of accuracy and precision of the CDI are automatically changed from high precision on departure, lower precision enroute, and medium to high precision on arrival and approach.

The three navigation modes and their corresponding CDI deflections are:

- Enroute (ENRT) Mode – 2.0 nm full scale CDI deflection

- Terminal (TERM) Mode – 1.0 nm full scale CDI deflection

- Approach (APP) Mode – 0.3 nm full scale CDI deflection (or 2° at the final approach fix, whichever is less)

Your flight will start in terminal mode, transition to enroute mode as you depart, then transition back to terminal and then to approach mode as you get closer to your destination. The current mode is displayed in one of the default data blocks on the IFD navigator. In the example below, the IFD540 shows that it is in approach mode, as shown in the data block on the left side of the display.

Note: The Nav Mode box is one of the "datablocks" that can be displayed on the IFD5XX/4XX. Datablocks are completely configurable by the pilot; you can choose which boxes to display and where to display them. This will be discussed in Lesson 11. It is a good idea to display the Nav Mode box on the permanent (left) side of the IFD540 display so you always have full situational awareness.

Figure 9 - 5 Approach Mode Shown in Nav Mode Datablock

System Setup for Automatic Tuning, Capture, and Missed Approach

Before starting to fly instrument approaches, you should ensure that your IFD is set up to handle them properly. This is done using the **SETUP** tab under the **AUX** pages. The setup should be done in the IFD540 simulator for our training exercises and in the actual IFD navigator in your airplane. The settings shown are the factory defaults, so they're probably set this way already. But it doesn't hurt to make sure.

> Note: As is the case with most IFD5XX/4XX functions, you have complete flexibility to set these parameters any way that you'd like. The settings shown below are recommended. Change them only if you have a good reason to do so.

This section only discusses a few settings. The **SETUP** page will be explored further in a later chapter.

The settings affecting instrument approaches and their recommended values are:

- FMS: Advisory Glideslope – On: An advisory glideslope will be displayed for GPS approaches that do not have a published glideslope.

- FMS: Auto Enable Missed – On: The missed approach procedure will be automatically activated when the aircraft crosses the missed approach point.

- RADIO: Auto VLOC Tuning – On: VOR and localizer frequencies will be tuned automatically.

- RADIO: GPS → VLOC – Auto: The IFD navigator will automatically transition from GPS to VLOC navigation when certain capture criteria are met.

To change these settings to the desired values, use the following procedure:

- ☑ Start the IFD540 or IFD440 simulator.

- ☑ Press the **AUX** rocker to select the **SETUP** tab.

☑ Under the **FMS** category, scroll down with the touch screen or the **IFD Multi-Function** knob to display **Advisory Glideslope** and **Auto Enable Missed**.

☑ Under the **Radio** category, use the touch screen or the **IFD Multi-Function** knob to set **Auto-VLOC Tuning** and **Auto GPS-->VLOC Capture**.

☑ Make sure that the four setup items described above are set to the appropriate values. If one is not, select it, and then turn the inner (small) **IFD Multi-Function** knob to change the value.

Figure 9 - 6 Setting the Approach Options on the Setup Tab

General Approach Procedures

The best way to execute instrument approaches consistently is to establish a standard procedure that you use whenever you shoot an approach. By doing things the same way every time you establish habits and a flow pattern. Once the habit is established you don't leave anything out. You can use whatever method you want, as long as it covers everything and you always do it the same.

The standard procedure for instrument approaches that will be used for the following training exercises is:

1. Set up your flight plan in the IFD, including the origin airport, enroute waypoints, and destination airport.

2. When you know the landing runway and the approach in use, program the IFD with the expected approach and its transition.

3. When cleared by ATC, go direct to the appropriate approach fix or activate the appropriate leg of the approach.

4. Confirm the approach minimums from the approach chart that correspond to the expected navigation source state displayed on the IFD.

5. As the approach proceeds, confirm that:

    a. The IFD transitions from ENRT to TERM to APP navigation mode before you cross the final approach fix.

    b. The appropriate VOR or localizer frequency is auto-tuned (if applicable), as you intercept the final approach course.

6. At the missed approach point, apply power, re-configure the aircraft for climb, and confirm that the IFD has automatically transitioned to the missed approach procedure and GPS navigation state.

All this will become clearer as you go through the practice scenarios given below.

Instrument Approach Scenarios

To learn about instrument approach procedures, imagine that you are practicing for your instrument proficiency check (IPC) in the Oshkosh area. You will depart from the Fond du Lac (KFLD) airport and fly in the vicinity of the Oshkosh (KOSH), Appleton (KATW) and Green Bay (KGRB) airports, shooting instrument approaches as you go.

GPS Full Approach with NOPT Initial Segment and Missed Approach

For your first practice approach, you will depart from the Fond du Lac airport and fly the RNAV (GPS) 3 approach into Appleton, shown below. This will be a full approach, without radar vectors from ATC. You will fly over the Oshkosh VOR (OSH), using the OSH transition. This transition is marked "NoPT" on the chart, meaning that a course reversal at the APIXE waypoint is not required.

The approach will terminate with a missed approach.

The minimums box for this approach shows several different values for different aircraft navigational abilities. Minimum values for LPV, LNAV/VNAV, and LNAV are all shown. You will need to know your IFD's navigation source state before you can decide which approach minimums to use. Normally you would expect this to be an LPV approach. However, it could be different if, for example, you were not receiving a WAAS signal.

The routing you will initially use for this flight is KFLD OSH KATW.

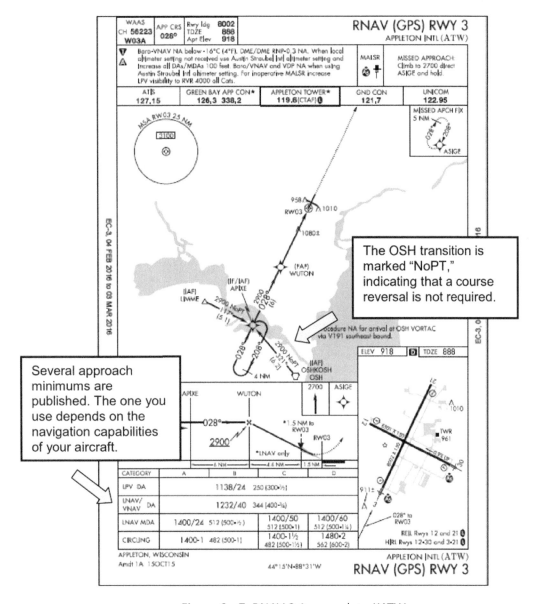

Figure 9 - 7 RNAV 3 Approach to KATW

Proceed as follows:

☑ Start the IFD540 simulator program on your iPad.

☑ Build the **KFLD OSH KATW** flight plan on the **FPL** page.

☑ Press the **Activate Flight Plan** line select key.

The simulated aircraft will take off and start flying from KFLD to OSH.

Very soon after takeoff you get the weather information at Appleton. ATC tells you to expect the GPS approach to runway 3, using the Oshkosh transition. It's time for you to set up the approach on your IFD.

Take these steps:

☑ Press the **PROC** key on the right side of the display. **PROC** stands for "Procedure." It's the button you press to select an instrument approach procedure.

☑ A list of instrument approaches for your destination airport, KATW, will be displayed. Use the touch screen or the **IFD Multi-Function** knob to select the **RNAV 3** approach.

Lesson 9: Instrument & Visual Approaches

☑ Press the **ENTR** key.

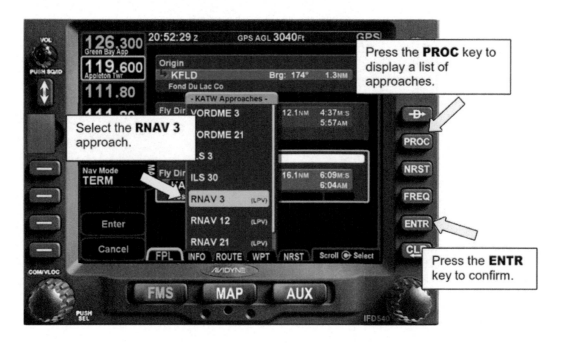

Figure 9 - 8 Selecting the RNAV 3 Approach

☑ A list of transitions for the RNAV 3 approach will be displayed. Select the **OSH** transition.

☑ Press the **ENTR** key.

☑ Tap the **MAP** tab to display the flight plan page map, if it's not displayed already.

Figure 9 - 9 Selecting the OSH Transition

The flight plan and the associated map now show that the RNAV 3 approach has been added to your flight plan. You selected the OSH transition. The OSH waypoint was already part of your flight plan, so the transition was simply inserted between OSH and KATW. If OSH had not already been part of your flight plan it would have been inserted. However, the IFD would not have known how to get to OSH, so a flight plan gap would also have been inserted. This will be demonstrated in a later part of this lesson.

OSH is shown as a "NoPT" transition on the approach plate. The IFD is aware of this, so no course reversal was added to your route. You will proceed directly from OSH to APIXE, which is an intermediate fix on the approach.

Note: You could have selected APIXE as the approach transition. If you had done that, a course reversal holding pattern would have been added to the approach. This would have happened because APIXE is not designated as a NoPT transition.

Figure 9 - 10 Flight Plan with RNAV 3 Approach

Your flight will proceed from its present position to OSH and will fly the approach with no further input from you. As it progresses, observe the following:

☑ After you cross the OSH waypoint, the **GPS→LPV** caption will appear in the navigation source state window. This indicates that your IFD has LPV navigation accuracy and will transition to LPV mode when it begins the approach. An LPV approach provides a protected glide slope to decision altitude and is functionally equivalent to an ILS approach. You should select LPV minimums from the minimums table on the approach plate.

☑ The navigation mode window on the left of the display shows that you are still in **TERM** mode. This is because you are not yet aligned with the final approach course.

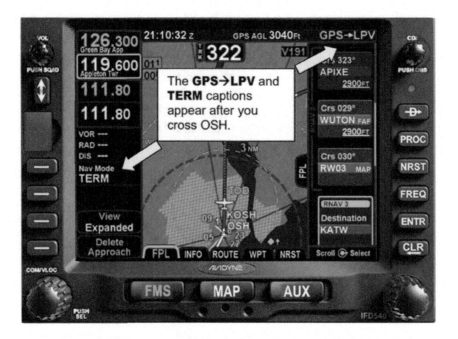

Figure 9 - 11 Indications on First Part of Approach

☑ When you cross APIXE and begin the final approach course, the navigation source state window shows that you have now transitioned to LPV mode.

☑ At the same time, the navigation mode window shows that you are now in APP mode. At this point the course deviation indicator in your aircraft would have transitioned to its highest sensitivity and you would be ready to shoot the approach.

CAUTION: It is extremely important that you ensure that your IFD has gone into APP mode and is displaying the navigation source state (LPV, in this case) that you are expecting. This is the only way that you know that your GPS receiver has the required accuracy for the approach, and you are using the correct approach minimums.

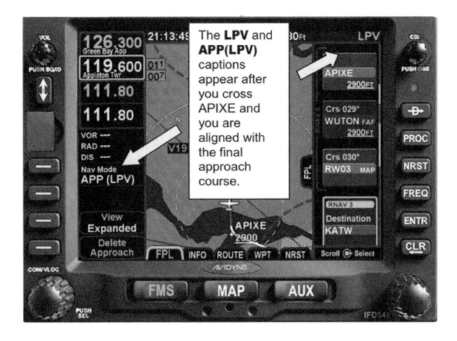

Figure 9 - 12 Final Approach Indications

☑ The simulated aircraft will track inbound, following the approach course until it reaches the missed approach point.

Note: The IFD540 simulator will track the lateral inbound course but will not simulate the descent for the approach. This is an LPV approach. In a real aircraft you would receive guidance on your glide slope indicator and you would follow it just as you would on an ILS approach.

The missed approach point is the RW03 waypoint. When you reach this position in a real aircraft you would immediately add power and reconfigure the aircraft for a climb.

The IFD will provide guidance for the missed approach. When you reach the missed approach point and have established a stable climb, look at your IFD and confirm that it is:

• Following the missed approach portion of the flight plan.

• Using GPS as the navigation source state.

• Using the TERM navigation mode.

At this point you can re-engage the autopilot for your missed approach.

The figure below shows the IFD immediately after the missed approach point.

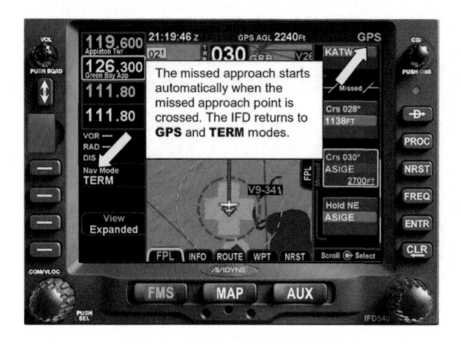

Figure 9 - 13 Missed Approach Indications

The IFD will fly the missed approach procedure to the holding waypoint. There it will use the appropriate holding pattern entry procedure to enter the hold. It will remain in the hold until you take further action.

GPS Full Approach with Course Reversal Hold

Your next practice approach will be the ATW RNAV GPS 3 once again. After missing the previous approach, you are holding at the missed approach holding fix. You will depart the hold and proceed to the initial approach point for the approach.

This approach will be the same as the one you just did, except for one thing: You're coming from the opposite direction than you did before. You'll have to perform a course reversal holding pattern, as published on the chart, before you begin the approach.

Proceed as follows:

☑ Press the **PROC** key to select a new procedure. A list of KATW approaches will appear.

☑ Select the **RNAV 3** approach, just as you did before.

Figure 9 - 14 Selecting the RNAV 3 Approach

☑ Press the **ENTR** key to accept the approach. A list of transitions will appear.

☑ Select the **APIXE** transition.

☑ Press the **ENTR** key to accept it. A box will appear asking you to confirm.

Figure 9 - 15 Selecting the APIXE Transition

☑ Press the **ENTR** key again to confirm that you want to replace the active approach.

Lesson 9: Instrument & Visual Approaches

Figure 9 - 16 Confirming the New Approach

As soon as you accept the new approach the IFD simulator will turn to exit the hold and proceed direct to the APIXE waypoint. In a real aircraft, you would probably control your heading manually and go direct to APIXE when ATC clears you to do so.

Figure 9 - 17 Starting the New Approach

When the simulated aircraft reaches APIXE it will automatically enter the course reversal hold depicted on the approach plate.

Lesson 9: Instrument & Visual Approaches

Note that the message **Exiting Hold at Fix** appears in the lower right corner of the display. This indicates that, unlike the holding patterns you have seen so far, you will not remain in this hold. This hold is only for course reversal purposes so the IFD will automatically exit the hold when you cross the holding fix inbound.

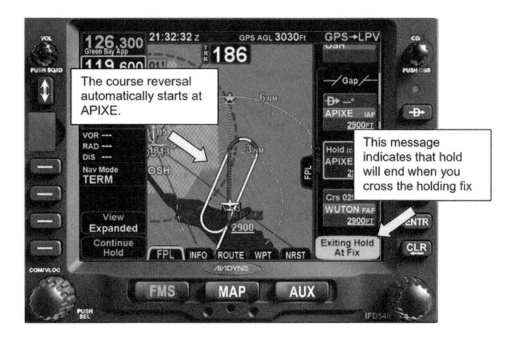

Figure 9 - 18 Entering the Course Reversal Hold

You can confirm that you will exit the hold by noting that the leg after the hold is displayed as a barber pole, indicating that it is the next leg to be flown.

There are times, however, when you would want to remain in the hold. This could happen, for example, if you had not been cleared for the approach and you had to wait in the hold until another aircraft left the airspace. In that case you would press the **Continue Hold** line select key. You would then remain in the hold indefinitely until you took further action to exit the hold using one of the methods explained in a previous chapter.

When you exit the hold you will be aligned properly with the final approach course. Fly the approach as you did in the previous example.

Note: The IFD will always insert a course reversal hold if one is depicted on the approach plate and you are not flying a NoPT transition. However, ATC can clear you for a straight-in approach if you are arriving at the holding fix at less than a 90 degree angle from the final approach course (AIM 5-4-6.e.6). In that case you would not want to fly the holding pattern at all. You can skip the hold before you enter it by simply deleting it from your flight plan with the **CLR** key, as discussed in the lesson on holding patterns. (You cannot delete procedure turns. This will be discussed in a later section.)

Figure 9 - 19 Proceeding Inbound on the Approach

VOR Approach with a Procedure Turn and an Alternate Airport

The next exercise will demonstrate how the IFD handles VOR approaches and procedure turns. You will also learn how to add an alternate airport to your flight plan.

You will fly the VOR 27 approach to Oshkosh. This will be another full approach, using a procedure turn as a course reversal. You will depart from Fond du Lac (KFDL) and proceed direct to the Oshkosh airport (KOSH). Then you will fly the full approach and terminate it with a missed approach.

This flight will also include an alternate airport, KATW, which is located just north of KOSH. After missing the approach at Oshkosh you will enter the published holding pattern. Then you will proceed to KATW in the next part of this lesson.

The approach plate is shown below. The only transition for this approach is over the OSH VOR. The only way to get established on the approach is to receive radar vectors to the final approach course or to fly the procedure turn. For this exercise we will assume that Milwaukee Approach radar is out of service, so the procedure turn is your only option.

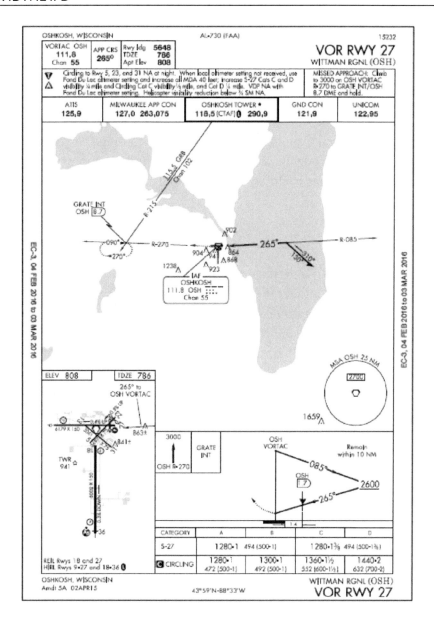

Figure 9 - 20 The VOR 27 Approach to KOSH

Adding an Alternate Airport to the Flight Plan

Before beginning the approach you will add an alternate airport to your flight plan. The general procedure for doing so is:

1. Build a normal flight plan to the destination airport.

2. Add the routing from the destination to the alternate airport.

3. Add the alternate airport to the end of flight plan.

This means that you have now two destinations in your flight plan: The initial destination airport and the alternate. So when you press the PROC key to select an approach, how does the IFD know which airport to use?

The answer is simple: When a flight plan contains multiple airports, each press of the **PROC** key displays approaches for a different airport. So you can have as many airports in a flight plan as you would like. When you want to add an approach to one of them, just press the **PROC** key several times until the approaches for the correct airport are displayed. Then select the approach and transition. The approach's waypoints will be added to your flight plan.

You can also add an approach for each airport in the flight plan, including the waypoints for all of them. This would be useful if you wanted to pre-load your destination and several alternates before takeoff to reduce your in-flight workload. Any of the approaches could be flown by going direct to the appropriate waypoint or activating the appropriate leg.

> **Note:** A flight plan can also have multiple instances of the same airport (for shooting multiple practice approaches) but a flight plan can't contain the same point twice in a row. There must be at least one other waypoint between each instance of the same airport. Setting up an approach would add those in-between waypoints, so you could program several approaches in a row to the same airport.

Flying the VOR 27 Approach

Let's see how all this works by flying another practice approach.

Your initial clearance is KFDL direct to KOSH. Your alternate airport is KATW. After you miss the approach at KOSH you will fly the published missed approach procedure then go directly to KATW.

Your IFD flight plan will be KFLD KOSH KATW. This is a very simple flight plan because there are no enroute waypoints between any of the airports.

Proceed as follows:

- ☑ Shut down and restart the IFD540 simulator on your iPad.
- ☑ Build the **KFLD KOSH KATW** flight plan on the **FPL** page.
- ☑ Press the **Activate Flight Plan** line select key.

The simulated aircraft will take off and start flying from KFLD to KOSH. As soon as it does:

- ☑ Press the **PROC** key. A list of KOSH approaches will appear. (If KATW approaches are displayed instead, press the **PROC** key again.)
- ☑ Select the **VOR 27** approach.
- ☑ Press the **ENTR** key.
- ☑ Select the **OSH** transition.
- ☑ Press the **ENTR** key.

Figure 9 - 21 Selecting the VOR 27 Approach

The approach has now been added to your flight plan, but there is a problem. A flight plan gap has been placed between the KOSH airport and the OSH waypoint. Even though the Oshkosh airport and the Oshkosh VOR are in almost the same place, they are not the same thing. You told the IFD to use the OSH transition so it added the OSH waypoint to the flight plan, but didn't know how to get there from the airport, so it added a gap.

This seems pretty trivial but it's not. It is very common that gaps appear when you add an approach to a flight plan. This happens when you select a transition waypoint that's not already on your flight plan, or you select radar vectors to final (as we'll see later).

You must always inspect the flight plan after you add an approach and deal with any gaps. In this case, we'll fix the problem by going direct to the OSH waypoint, which begins the approach.

Another way to close the gap would be to press the **Activate Approach** line select key, which is shown in the figure below. But **Activate Approach** does slightly different things in different contexts, so you might get an unexpected surprise. It's better practice to maintain positive control by telling the IFD540 exactly what you want it do. In this case, you should tell it to proceed direct to OSH.

Figure 9 - 22 The Gap in the Flight Plan

Proceed as follows:

☑ Move the cursor to the **OSH** waypoint.

☑ Press the **Direct** key.

☑ Press the **ENTR** key twice to confirm.

Figure 9 - 23 Going Direct to the Initial Approach Fix

Your aircraft is now proceeding directly to the OSH waypoint. When it gets there it will begin the approach by turning outbound. It will then perform the procedure turn.

Before you start the procedure turn you should check the navigation source state of the IFD, as you did in the previous exercises. This time, note that:

- **GPS→VLOC** appears in the navigation source state window, indicating that the IFD will transition to VHF navigation when it begins the final approach.

- The OSH VOR frequency, **111.8**, has been automatically tuned and identified. (The VLOC IDENTIFIER data block can be used to display the station ID automatically. This will be discussed further in a later lesson.)

- **TERM** appears in the navigation mode window.

Figure 9 - 24 VOR Approach Indications

The simulated aircraft will now fly outbound, execute the procedure turn, and then proceed inbound.

On the inbound course you should look for the following indications:

- The navigation source state window should display **VLOC** in green, indicating VOR navigation.

- The navigation mode window should display **APP**, indicating that you are in approach mode.

The IFD540 simulator does not simulate VOR or ILS transmitters. Therefore, the simulated IFD540 will not make the switch from GPS→VLOC to VLOC, as a real IFD would. Instead, it will revert back to GPS mode when you cross the final approach fix. But GPS is not legal for flying a VOR approach that doesn't have a GPS overlay.

This behavior would happen in a real aircraft if the IFD did not transition properly to VLOC navigation. The unit will not go into VLOC mode unless you are on the final approach course, the VHF nav radio is tuned properly, the CDI needle is less than 50% full scale deviation, and the Morse code identifier has been decoded and matches the ID of the approach navaid.

Lesson 9: Instrument & Visual Approaches

If you are in the correct position and the CDI is displaying the proper indication, you can listen to the nav identifier code yourself and determine whether or not it is correct. If it is, you could select VLOC mode manually by turning the CDI knob in the upper right corner of the IFD.

This, however, is a bad time to be tuning and identifying radios. If you don't transition to VLOC mode it would be better to simply miss the approach and set things up properly when your workload is lower. Or you could try a different approach.

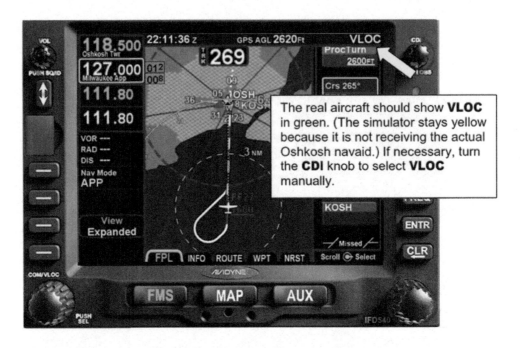

Figure 9 - 25 Indications on Final VOR Approach Course

After the simulated aircraft flies the procedure turn it will complete the approach, start the missed approach procedure, and proceed to the hold.

Let the aircraft enter the hold and remain there as you prepare for the next practice approach.

Figure 9 - 26 Holding After the VOR 27 Approach

Skipping A Procedure Turn

This exercise involved the use of a procedure turn. There are some instances where a procedure turn is part of an approach but you do not want to use it. For example, if you were receiving radar vectors and approaching Oshkosh from ten or fifteen miles east, you could be cleared for the straight-in VOR27 approach. You would want to intercept the final approach course a long way out and proceed inbound.

Unlike course reversal holds, you cannot simply use the **CLR** key to delete a procedure turn from an approach. You must "go around" it instead. There are two ways to do that:

1. Proceed direct to a waypoint after the procedure turn.

2. Activate the leg following the procedure turn.

For example, you could skip the Oshkosh VOR27 procedure turn by selecting the FF27 leg and pressing the **Activate Leg** line select key. This would cause you to intercept the final approach course outside FF27 and proceed inbound.

ILS Approach with Vectors to Final

The next approach will be an ILS approach with radar vectors to the final approach course. This is the most common type of approach used at large airports. The IFD makes it simple. Let's see how this works by continuing the scenario.

You are now holding at GRATE, the missed approach waypoint for the KOSH VOR 27 approach. Your alternate airport is KATW. It is already included in your flight plan.

You receive a clearance to the KATW airport, just north of your present position. You will get radar vectors to an ILS 3 approach. This approach will be flown to a missed approach.

Proceed as follows:

☑ Press the **PROC** key. Each time you press it, a list of approaches for a different airport will be displayed. Since you have two airports in your flight plan (KOSH and KATW), pressing the PROC key will alternate back and forth between the two. Press **PROC** until KATW approaches are displayed.

☑ Select the **ILS 3** approach to KATW.

☑ Press the **ENTR** key.

☑ Select the **Vectors** transition.

☑ Press the **ENTR** key again to confirm the selection.

Figure 9 - 27 Selecting the ILS 3 Approach to KATW

Examine the resulting flight plan. You will see that it now includes the ILS 3 approach, which begins with a way-point called **VTF**. This stands for "vectors to final." The approach is in your flight plan, but it's not active yet. You will stay in the holding pattern until you take further action. You will do this by activating the vectors to final portion of the flight plan.

Proceed as follows:

☑ Place the cursor on the **VTF** block in the flight plan.

☑ Press the **Activate VTF** line select key.

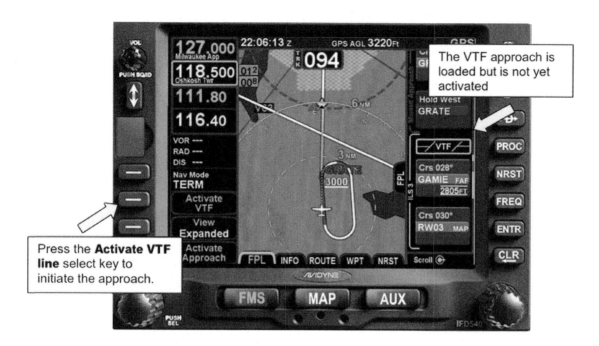

Figure 9 - 28 Activating a Vectors to Final Approach

The final approach leg of the ILS 3 approach to KATW is now active. The simulated aircraft will depart the hold and fly a course to intercept the approach. In a real aircraft you would fly headings assigned by ATC. The simulator does not allow you control its heading; it will pick its own course to intercept the approach.

Figure 9 - 29 Intercepting the ILS Final Approach Course

When the simulated aircraft intercepts the final approach course it will turn to proceed inbound. As before, you should look at the IFD's indications and ensure that it is flying the approach properly. These include:

Lesson 9: Instrument & Visual Approaches

- The nav radio should automatically tune to **109.1**, the KATW ILS 3 frequency.

- The navigation source state window should display **VLOC** in green, indicating ILS navigation. (The simulator will not do this.)

- The navigation mode window should display **APP**, indicating that you are in approach mode.

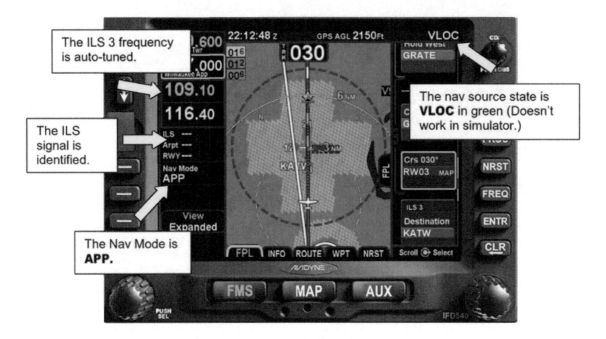

Figure 9 - 30 ILS Approach Indications

Retrying an Approach

Whenever you fly a missed approach procedure after shooting a vectors-to-final approach the IFD provides an easy way to go back and fly the same approach over again without going to the trouble of reselecting and reactivating it. This is the **Retry Approach** line select key, shown below.

> **Note:** The Retry Approach feature is only available when you are executing a missed approach after flying a vectors-to-final approach.

To use the Retry Approach key, do the following:

- ☑ Press the **Retry Approach** line select key.

- ☑ As soon as you press the **Retry Approach** key the vectors-to-final transition for the current approach will be activated. You would then follow ATC's headings to re-intercept the final approach course. The simulator will fly its own headings to intercept.

Press the **Retry Approach** line select key to reactivate the approach.

Figure 9 - 31 The Retry Approach Line Select Key

Simulated aircraft is now on vectors to re-intercept the final approach course.

Figure 9 - 32 ILS Approach After Reactivation

Flying a DME Arc to a VOR/DME Approach

The last approach exercise you will fly will include a DME arc transition to a VOR/DME approach.

For this approach you will leave the Oshkosh area and go to Kansas. You will fly from Lyons (KLYO) to Hutchinson (KHUT), using the VOR/DME 22 approach. You will be arriving from the northwest, transitioning via the 15 DME arc. This is a NoPT transition.

Lesson 9: Instrument & Visual Approaches

The relevant portion of the approach plate is shown below.

> **Note:** The IFD does not contain a DME receiver. But you may fly this approach because GPS is a legal substitute for DME. You must, however, use VOR navigation on the final approach course.

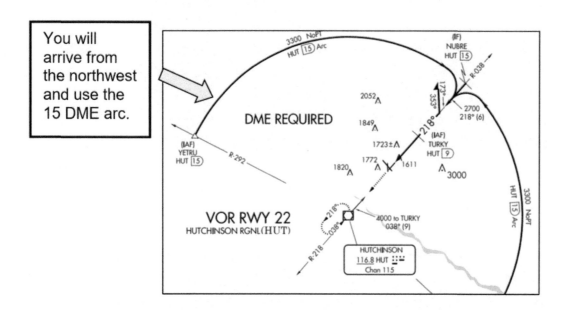

Figure 9 - 33 VOR/DME Approach with DME Arc

Proceed as follows:

☑ Shut down and restart the IFD540 simulator on your iPad.

☑ Build the **KLYO KHUT** flight plan on the **FPL** page.

☑ Press the **Activate Flight Plan** line select key.

The simulated aircraft will take off and start flying from KLYO to KHUT. As soon as it does:

☑ Press the **PROC** key on the right side of the display

☑ Select the **VORDME 22** approach.

☑ Press the **ENTR** key.

☑ Select the **YETRU** transition. **YETRU** is the initial approach fix that begins on the east side of the 15 DME arc. If you were unsure of this you could see that it's the appropriate arc by looking at the **Preview-Approach** map on the **FPL** page, as shown below.

☑ Press the **ENTR** key.

Figure 9 - 34 Selecting the VOR/DME 22 Approach to KHUT

The VOR/DME 22 approach has been added to the flight plan but a gap has also been added. You are still flying direct to KHUT, as you were before. You receive the following clearance from ATC:

"Cleared direct to the Hutchinson airport, intercept the 15 DME arc, cleared for the VOR/DME 22 approach."

How can you execute this clearance? The present leg you are flying clearly intercepts the DME arc, but there's no waypoint at the intersection point. The arc is still shown in white, meaning that it's not the next leg. How can you turn to intercept it? You could go direct to the waypoint that begins the arc, but that would be a big waste of time and would violate your clearance.

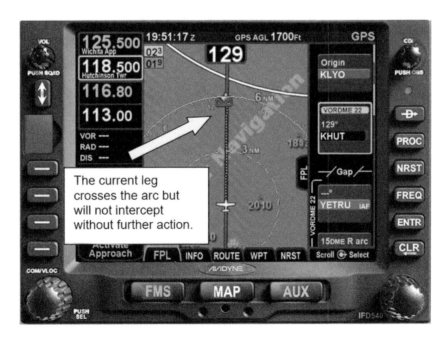

Figure 9 - 35 The Current Flight Plan and the DME Arc

The trick is to activate the DME arc leg just before you intercept it. Use this procedure:

☑ Keep flying the present leg until you get within a mile or two of the DME arc. You can estimate the distance by looking at the range rings on the display.

☑ When you get close to the arc, move the cursor to the **15DME R arc** flight plan box.

☑ Press the **Activate Leg** line select key.

> Note: Once the arc leg is activated, the IFD immediately turns (left in this case) to intercept the arc at a tangent angle; it does not continue straight ahead to the nearest point on the arc. If the arc leg is activated from too far away, the turn (to the tangent point on the arc from your current position) will be contrary to your ATC clearance and might not avoid obstacles.

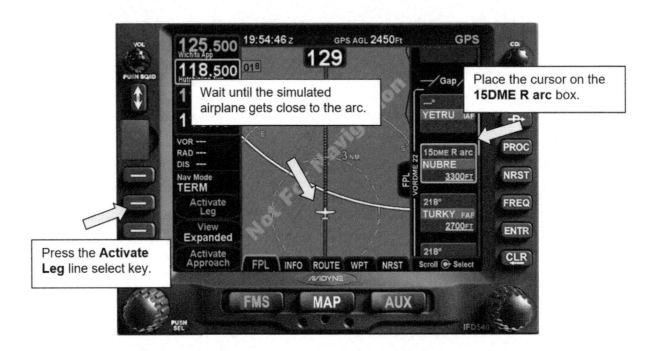

Figure 9 - 36 Intercepting the DME Arc

This will make the DME arc the current leg. It will be colored magenta. The simulated aircraft will turn left to intercept and track the arc. It will then turn right to the final approach course when it reaches the lead in radial, as shown below.

Figure 9 - 37 After Arc Interception

Visual Approaches

The IFD provides advisory guidance for conducting Visual Approaches. How the approach path is presented depends on several factors:

- How the Visual Approach preferences are configured in the setup menu

- The runway selected for the Visual Approach

- The type of approach entry selected

- Model of IFD in use

A full description of how to enable and set preferences for Visual Approaches is covered in Lesson 11.

To learn about Visual Approach procedures, imagine that you are flying on an IFR flight from Long Beach, CA (KLGB) to the Carlsbad - Palomar Airport (KCRQ) in June - a time of year that is typically foggy in the Coastal Southern CA area. The preflight weather forecast indicated for your time of arrival the weather will be **"500 OVC and 1 mile visibility"** so you are prepared to fly an instrument approach. 20 miles out from KCRQ, you check ATIS and the current observation is **"Scattered clouds at 2000' and 10nm visibility with fog to the west, Visual Approaches are in use. Landing and departing on runway 24."**

When you hear that Visual Approaches are in use, select Visual Approach as the approach type:

☑ Press the PROC key on the right side of the display. PROC stands for "Procedure". It's the button you press to select the Visual Approach procedure.

☑ A list of instrument approach procedures for your destination airport (KCRQ) will be displayed. Use the touch screen or the IFD multi-function know to select the Visual 24.

☑ Press the ENTR key.

☑ A list of Visual Entries for the Visual 24 approach will be displayed.

Lesson 9: Instrument & Visual Approaches

☑ Select the desired pattern entry type. For this Lesson, we'll select Right Downwind. A preview of the approach will appear on the MAP page.

☑ Press the ENTR key.

☑ Tap the MAP tab to display the flight plan page map, if it's not displayed already.

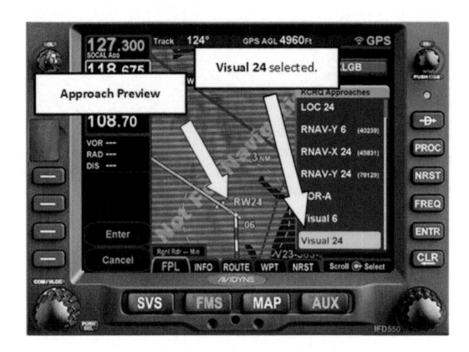

Figure 9 - 38 Visual 24 Selected

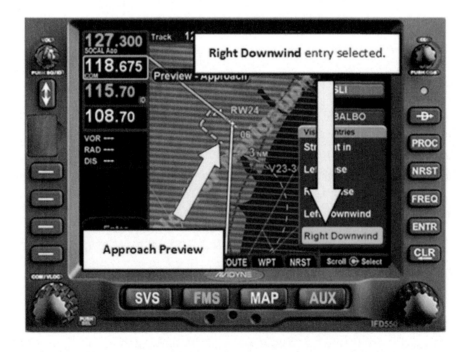

Figure 9 - 39 Right Downwind Entry Selected

When you switch to the final approach controller, you are provided vectors for a visual approach. 10 nm from the airport, you report that you have visual contact on the airport and are cleared for the Visual Approach.

☑ From the FMS display, touch "Activate Visual". This should resolve the gap in the flight plan.

☑ Ensure that the word "Visual" appears in the top right of the display.

Figure 9 - 40 Activate Visual

Figure 9 - 41 Visual Approach Activated

The MAP display will show the selected traffic pattern entry for the runway that was selected. Manually fly the visual approach using the traffic pattern display as a positional reference. When on the final approach leg, the IFD will provide lateral and vertical guidance. Pilots using the IFD545 or IFD550 can see the lateral and vertical guidance on the SVS display. Vertical guidance will discontinue when the aircraft reaches .1nm from the runway threshold.

Figure 9 - 42 Lateral and Vertical Guidance on Visual Approach (IFD550 and IFD545 only)

IFD440 Differences

All the approach procedures that have been explored in this lesson work exactly the same way on the IFD440 as they do on the IFD550 and IFD540. The only difference is that the IFD440 has a much smaller screen. But the small screen means that it doesn't display as much information, so you have to work harder to find it.

This includes:

☑ The IFD440 does not display navigation and communication frequencies at the same time. You must still verify that the correct nav frequency has been tuned. Press the **COMM/VLOC** knob to do this.

☑ There is no room to display the navigation mode on the left side of the display. You should use the **Data Block** feature to display it on the right side of the **MAP** page.

See the discussion of datablocks in Lesson 11 for more ideas on how to display approach information on the IFD440.

Lesson 9: Instrument & Visual Approaches

Figure 9 - 42 IFD440 Approach Indications

IFD545, IFD510, and IFD410 Differences

The IFD545, IFD510, and IFD410 do not contain VHF navigation receivers. Therefore, they cannot perform ILS, localizer, or VOR based approaches.

They fly GPS approaches in the same way as the IFD550, IFD540, and IFD440 navigators.

Lesson Review

IFD5XX/4XX Approach Capabilities

- The Avidyne IFD550, IFD540, and IFD440 contain both VHF and GPS WAAS navigation receivers.

- The IFD545, IFD510, and IFD410 contain only GPS receivers.

- The IFD550 and IFD545 provide HDI and VDI guidance on the SVS display.

- IFD550, IFD540, and IFD440 will fly most modern VHF approaches (VOR, ILS, and localizer), even those that "require" DME in most cases.

- All IFD models will fly the following types of GPS approaches;

    - LNAV

    - LNAV+V

    - LNAV/VNAV

    - LPV

    - LP

    - LP+V

- The type of the approach will affect its minimums and obstacle clearance criteria. Refer to the approach plate for the appropriate values.

Lesson 9: Instrument & Visual Approaches

- All IFD models support Visual Approaches.

- You can tell what kind of approach is being flown by looking at the Navigation Source State Window in the upper right corner of the IFD display.

- The sensitivity of a CDI attached to a IFD will change according to which Navigation Mode is being used. The CDI is more sensitive when it is close to an airport and less sensitive during the enroute part of the flight.

- The Navigation Modes and their corresponding sensitivities are:

  - Enroute Mode – 2.0 nm full scale CDI deflection

  - Terminal Mode – 1.0 nm full scale CDI deflection

  - Approach Mode – 0.3 nm full scale CDI deflection (or 2° at the FAF)

- The IFD will provide guidance for all parts of an approach, including holding patterns, procedure turns, DME arcs, vectors-to-final, and missed approaches.

Flying Instrument Approaches

- The standard procedure for instrument approaches is:

  1. Set up the flight plan in the IFD, including the origin airport, enroute waypoints, and destination airport.

  2. When you know the landing runway and the approach in use, program the IFD with the expected approach and its transition.

  3. When cleared by ATC, go direct to the approach fix or activate the appropriate leg of the approach.

  4. Confirm the approach minimums from the approach chart that correspond to the expected navigation source state displayed on the IFD.

  5. As the approach proceeds, confirm that:

     a. The IFD transitions from ENRT to TERM to APP navigation mode before you cross the final approach fix.

     b. The appropriate VOR or localizer frequency is auto-tuned (if applicable), as you intercept the final approach course.

     c. The appropriate navigation source state for the approach is displayed in the navigation source state window.

  6. At the missed approach point, apply power, re-configure the aircraft for climb, and confirm that the IFD has automatically transitioned to the missed approach procedure and GPS navigation state.

- The PROC (procedure) key is used to program an instrument approach.

- After pressing the PROC key, select the approach and transition that is to be used.

- The approach will be added to the flight plan. If the transition selected does not begin with a waypoint that is already in the flight plan, a gap will be inserted.

- The gap should be closed by going direct to an approach waypoint or activating an approach leg.

- Course reversals will be automatically included in instrument approaches unless a NoPT or vectors to final transition is selected.

- Holding pattern course reversals can be deleted from approaches, but procedure turns cannot.

- You can skip a procedure turn, if appropriate, by going direct to another approach waypoint or activating the leg after the procedure turn.

- An approach flown with a vectors-to-final transition can be reflown by pressing the **Retry** Approach line select key after the missed approach has been initiated.

- DME arcs can be intercepted by waiting until you are close to the arc, then using the Activate Leg line select key to activate the arc.

Multiple Destination Airports in a Flight Plan

- A flight plan can include more than one destination airport. This is useful for pre-planning alternates.

- Each destination airport can have an approach associated with it.

- A flight plan can also have multiple instances of the same airport (for shooting multiple practice approaches) but since a flight plan can't contain the same point twice in a row, there must be at least one other waypoint between each instance of the same airport.

- To add an approach to an airport, press the PROC key. Each time you press it a list of approaches for a different destination airport will be displayed. Stop pressing when you see the airport you want, then select the appropriate approach and transition.

Flying Visual Approaches

- A Visual Approach discontinuity always precedes a visual approach and cannot be removed

- Visual approaches are non-precision for use in VMC only and are intended to provide enhanced situational awareness and more stablized approach.

- A visual approach is flown the same way as LNAV+V (i.e. including advisory vertical deviations). However, the glideslope angle is controlled by a user setting.

- Advisory vertical guidance will be provided until the aircraft reaches a point 0.1nm from the runway threshold.

- During a visual approach, the Nav Mode datablock will display "Visual" for the approach type

- If there are no legs in the flight plan after the destination associated with a visual approach, the visual approach will remain active even after passing the runway threshold allowing you to stay in a closed traffic pattern and continue to receive guidance to the final approach course without ever touching the FMS

Lesson 10: Information and Utilities

In the previous lessons you learned how to use the IFD5XX/4XX to build and fly flight plans and to shoot instrument and visual approaches.

In addition to their navigation capabilities, the IFD units have the ability to help you with a variety of in-flight problems, like looking up airport information, ATC frequencies, performing E6B calculations, and running electronic checklists. This lesson will show you how to use these features.

At the end of the lesson you will know how to find information in the IFD's database and how to use the IFD timer, calculator, and checklist utilities.

The Scenario

You are back at the St. Paul Downtown Airport (KSTP), preparing for your trip to EAA AirVenture in Oshkosh (KOSH). You have already stored your flight plan in your IFD540 and loaded your passengers. Now it's time to look up the airport and ATC information you'll need for takeoff.

Proceed as follows:

- ☑ Start the IFD540 simulator program on your iPad.

- ☑ Use the ROUTE tab to activate the **OSH AIRVENTURE** flight plan you built in Lesson 7. If it's not there, build a KSTP EAU MAXMA WLCHS RIPON KOSH flight plan on the FPL tab.

- ☑ Press the **Activate Flight Plan** line select key.

- ☑ Pause the simulation by pressing the **Paused** button on the **Simulator** drop-down menu.

Getting Airport Information

You know from your weather briefing that the winds are favoring runway 31 for takeoff. You would like to look up the runway length to make sure it's long enough.

Do the following:

- ☑ Use the **FMS** rocker to display the FPL tab, if it's not displayed already.

- ☑ Move the cursor to the **KSTP** waypoint.

- ☑ Use the **FMS** rocker to select the INFO tab.

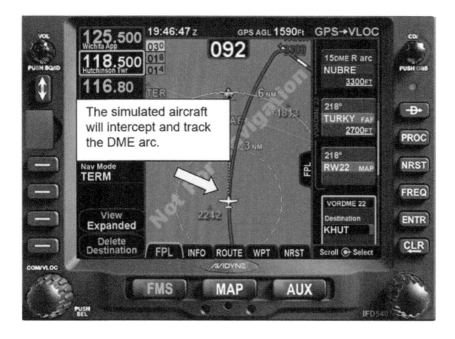

Figure 10 - 1 Selecting the FMS INFO Tab

The box at the top of the INFO tab should display **KSTP**. If it doesn't, move the cursor to it and use the touch screen keyboard to change it to **KSTP**.

The INFO tab is now displayed. It shows a variety of information about the St. Paul airport. The information is divided into several categories, each of which is contained in a separate box. The boxes are closed.

☑ Open the **General** box by tapping on it or moving the cursor to it and pressing the **ENTR** key. This box contains a variety of general information about the airport. Including its location, elevation, and the type of fuel available.

Figure 10 - 2 The KSTP Information Page

☑ Scroll up and down the box with the touch screen to see all the information.

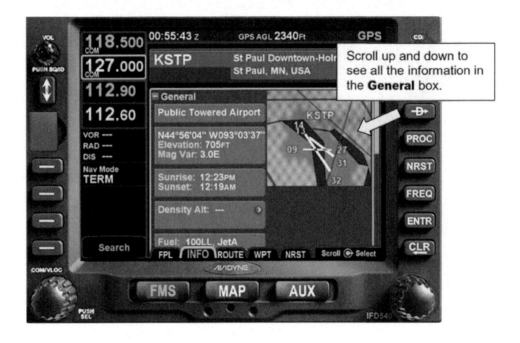

Figure 10 - 3 The General Information Box

☑ Close the **General** box by tapping on its title box or by moving the cursor to it and pressing the **ENTR** key.

☑ Open the **Runways** box by tapping on it or moving the cursor to it and pressing the **ENTR** key. This box contains information about runways at KSTP.

☑ Move the cursor to runway **13/31**. The runway will be displayed in cyan on the miniature airport diagram.

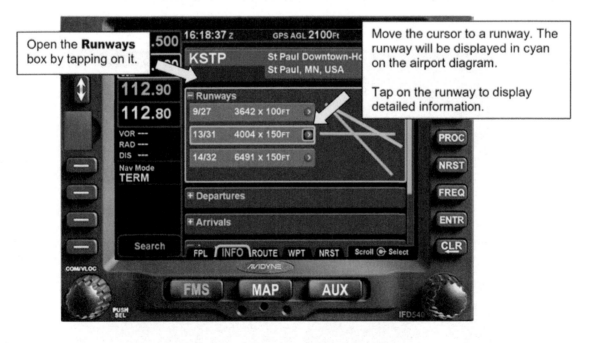

Figure 10 - 4 The Runway Information Box

☑ Tap on the runway **13/31** box, or press the **ENTR** key while the cursor is on the **13/31** box. A new box will be displayed which shows details about the runway. You can see its surface type, length, width, and compass bearing, among other things. Runway lights appear as small dots on the perimeter of the runway icon.

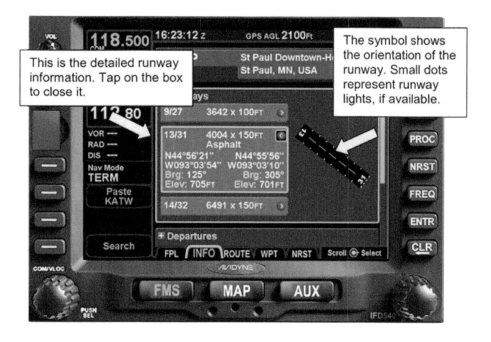

Figure 10 - 5 Detailed Runway Information

Finding information about your departure airport is good but it's not quite enough. You'd like to get information about the destination airport, KOSH, too. The IFD makes this easy. Do the following:

☑ Use the **FMS** rocker to select the FPL tab.

☑ Put the cursor on the destination airport, **KOSH**.

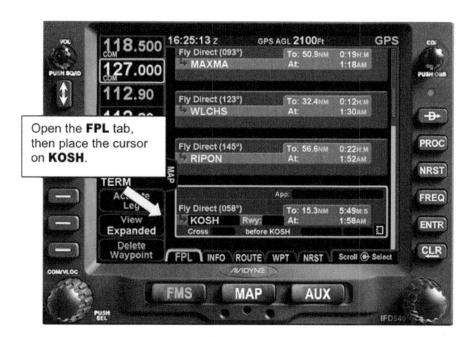

Figure 10 - 6 Selecting the Destination Airport

☑ Go back to the INFO tab. The information for KSTP should still be displayed. Press the **Paste KOSH** line select key. This will paste **KOSH** into the identifier field at the top of the screen.

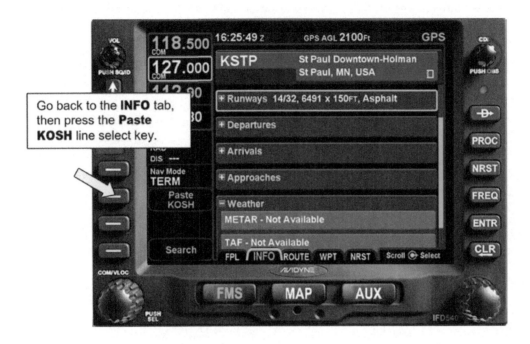

Figure 10 - 7 Pasting KOSH into the INFO Tab

Information for the Oshkosh airport is now displayed. You can review the runway information just as you did for the St. Paul airport.

Figure 10 - 8 The KOSH Information Page

Note: To display information for an airport or facility you can always enter the identifier into the box at the top of the display. This can be done with the touch-screen keyboard or the **IFD Multi-Function** knob, just as you would enter any other identifier. You can also use the **Paste** line select key. This key will paste the identifier that is currently selected by the cursor on the last page you looked at. You can also use the Search line select key, which will be explained below.

Finding Communications Frequencies

Now that you know the length of the runway you'll be using, it's time to look up the frequencies you'll need. These include the ATIS, clearance delivery, ground control, and tower frequencies.

There are two ways to find frequencies on the IFD540: The INFO tab and the **FREQ** button. The IFD440 does not have a **FREQ** button, so only the INFO tab is available. Let's look at the INFO tab first, since that is common to both units. Then we'll move on to the IFD540's **FREQ** button.

Using the INFO Tab

The INFO tab should already be displayed on your IFD540 simulator, since that's where you just looked up airport and runway information. If it's not, use the FMS rocker to bring it up.

Communications frequencies are contained in the Communications box on the INFO tab.

Do the following:

☑ Enter **KSTP** in the identifier window. You can put it in manually or use the **Paste KSTP** line select key.

☑ Open the **Communications** box by tapping on it or by moving the cursor to it and pressing the **ENTR** key. A list of all the frequencies associated with the St. Paul airport will appear.

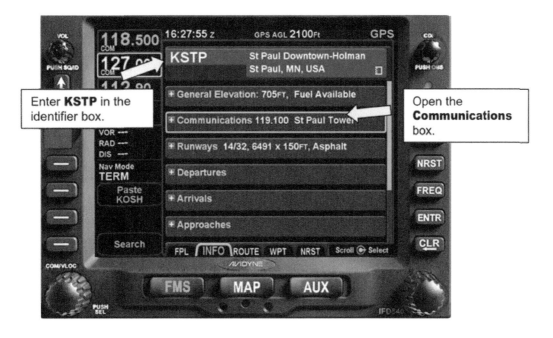

Figure 10 - 9 The INFO Communications Box

☑ Tap on the **ATIS** box twice, or move the cursor to it and press the **ENTR** key. The ATIS frequency will be placed in the standby frequency box, ready for you to activate it by pressing the **Frequency Swap** key.

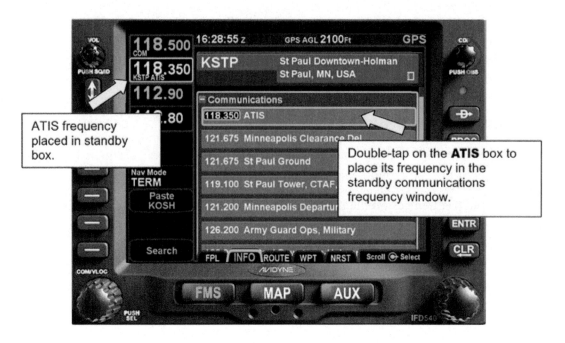

Figure 10 - 10 Loading the ATIS Frequency

You can load any of the frequencies in the Communications box in the same manner. Just double-tap on the frequency or place the cursor on it and press the **ENTR** key. Then press the Frequency Swap key. The frequency is now ready for use.

Using the FREQ Key (IFD540) or FREQ Page (IFD440)

The FREQ key is an easy way to find frequencies that you are most likely to need.

Do the following:

☑ Press the **FREQ** key, located on the right side of the IFD540 display. A new page showing three frequency tabs will now be displayed.

☑ Press **FREQ** again. Each time you press it a different frequency tab will be selected.

Figure 10 - 11 Using the FREQ Key

The three frequency tabs are:

1. **Airport** – The Airport tab contains the "most logical" frequencies associated with an airport. If you display it before takeoff or shortly after departure it will show frequencies for your origin airport. If you have proceeded more than five miles away from your origin, it will display frequency for your destination.

2. **Enroute** – The Enroute tab displays the most likely nearby ATC and FSS communications frequencies for your current geographic position.

3. **Recent** – The Recent tab shows the ten most recent frequencies that you have used. This would be useful if you wanted to go back to a previous frequency.

You can use any of the three tabs to automatically load frequencies into the standby frequency box. Simply double-tap on the desired frequency, or select the frequency with the cursor and press the **ENTR** key.

Note: The IFD440 does not have a **FREQ** key, but you can still access the FREQ page. It is displayed whenever you turn the COMM/VLOC frequency selector knob. Move between the three tabs by turning the outer **IFD Multi-Function** knob.

Finding Navigation Frequencies

Now that you've established the ATIS, ground, and tower frequencies for your flight to Oshkosh, it might be a good idea to look up some VOR frequencies. The EAU VOR is the first fix on your route. You should get that pre-tuned just in case you need it.

Note: The IFD will automatically tune each VOR in your flight plan. But it's not a bad idea to confirm that it was done correctly.

The procedure for looking up a navaid frequency is very similar to that used to find airport information.

Do the following:

☑ Bring up the FPL tab and place the cursor on the EAU waypoint.

Figure 10 - 12 Selecting the EAU Waypoint

☑ Use the **FMS** rocker to select the INFO tab.

☑ Press the **Paste EAU** line select key. The information page for EAU will be displayed.

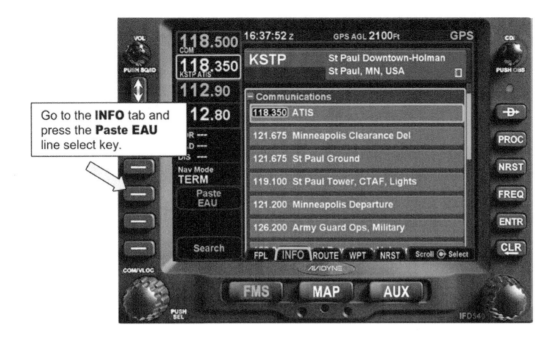

Figure 10 - 13 Pasting EAU into the INFO Tab

☑   Tap on the **EAU** frequency box, or place the cursor on it and press the **ENTR** key. The frequency will be loaded into the standby navigation frequency box. Press the **Frequency Swap** key to activate it.

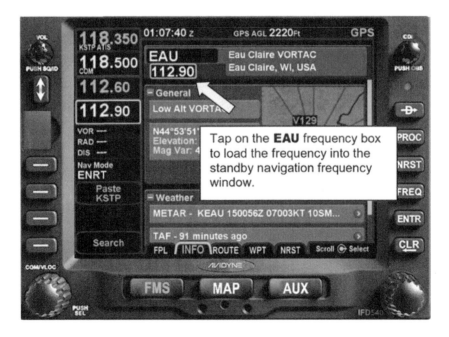

Figure 10 - 14 Loading the EAU VOR Frequency

Searching for Airports and Facilities

In the previous examples it was assumed that you knew the correct identifier for an airport or a facility. But what if you don't know the identifier? Then you can use the IFD's Search tool. It will let you search for all the airports and navaids associated with a specified city.

Let's say that you wanted to find information for the Chicago Midway airport, but you didn't know its identifier. Proceed as follows:

☑ Bring up the INFO tab on the display.

☑ Press the **Search** line select key. The Search dialog box will be displayed. You can use this box to enter the city, state, and type of facility you are searching for.

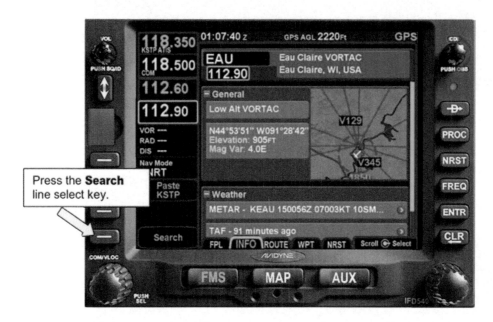

Figure 10 - 15 The Search Line Select Key

Figure 10 - 16 City Search Box

☑ Use the touch-screen keyboard or the IFD Multi-Function knob to enter **Chicago** in the **City** field.

☑ Double-tap on the **Kind** field to display a drop-down list. Select **Airport** from the list of options.

☑ Press the **ENTR** key. A list of all the airports in Chicago is displayed.

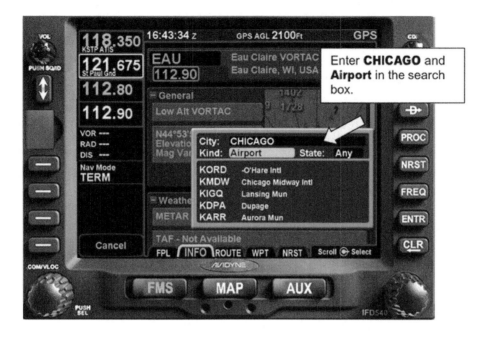

Figure 10 - 17 CHICAGO Search Entry

☑ Double-tap on the entry for the Chicago Midway airport, or place the cursor on it and press the **ENTR** key. The information page for KMDW will be displayed.

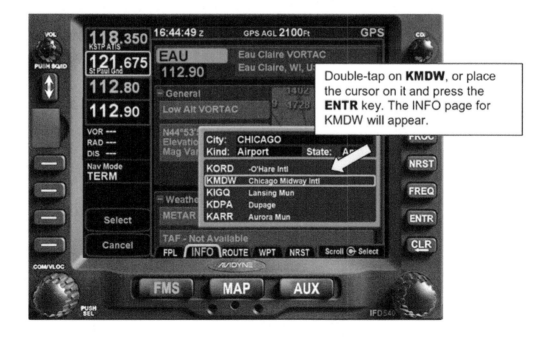

Figure 10 - 18 Selecting KMDW for the INFO Tab

Lesson 10: Information and Utilities

Finding Nearby Airports and Facilities

Let's continue with the current scenario, a flight from St. Paul Downtown airport to Oshkosh. Your pre-flight planning and frequency setup is now complete. It's time to take off.

After you're enroute it is always good to be able to quickly find a nearby airport or other facility. This could be extremely important in the event of an engine failure or emergency.

Do the following:

☑ Start the simulation by selecting the **Time X 1** button on the **Simulator** drop-down menu.

☑ Let the simulated airplane proceed for a few minutes until it leaves the terminal area.

☑ Press the **NRST** key (IFD540 only). A list of nearby airports, sorted by distance, will be displayed. The list that you see will be different from the one shown below. The airports shown will depend on the location of the simulated aircraft when you press the **NRST** key.

Figure 10 - 19 The NRST Key

☑ Move the cursor up and down the list of nearby airports. As you select each one, it will be highlighted in cyan on the display screen.

> **Note:** The IFD440 does not have a **NRST** key. Instead, use the **FMS** rocker to access the NRST tab. This is the same tab that appears when you press **NRST** on the IFD540.

> **Note:** Not all nearby airports are displayed. The airport list can be filtered by criteria such as runway length and surface type. You can set these criteria in the AUX → SETUP → SETUP MAP tab. Press the Filter line select key to remove the filter and display all nearby airports.

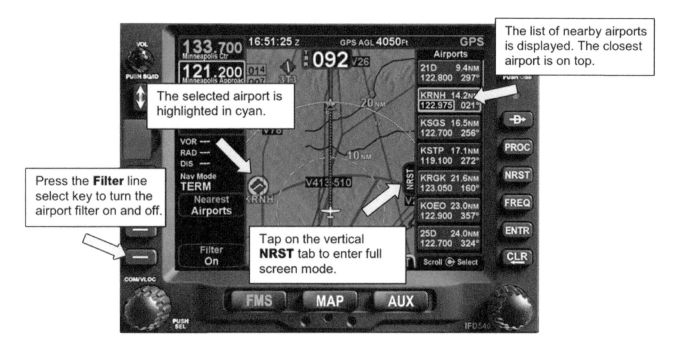

Figure 10 - 20 The NRST Tab

☑ Tap on the vertical NRST tab. This will change the **NRST** display to full-screen mode, which shows more information about each airport. You can also do the following with any of the airport boxes:

☑ Tapping on the blue ▢ symbol will bring up the INFO tab for the airport.

☑ Double-tapping on the frequency associated with the airport will load it into the standby frequency box. You can also do this by moving the cursor to the airport and pressing the **ENTR** key.

☑ Tap on the vertical MAP tab to return to the split screen mode.

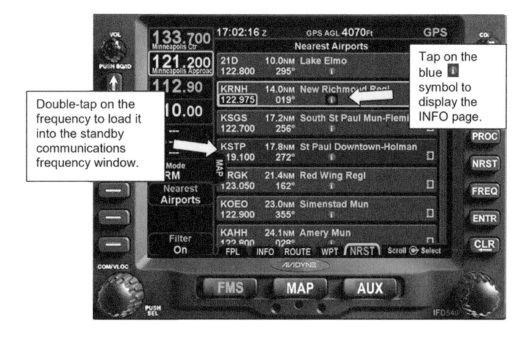

Figure 10 - 21 Using the NRST Tab

Lesson 10: Information and Utilities

☑ To go direct to one of the nearby airports, as you would if you had an emergency and wanted to land immediately, place the cursor on the airport and press the **Direct** key. The normal **Direct** pop-up box will appear. Confirm (if you want to) by pressing the **ENTR** key twice.

Figure 10 - 22 Going Direct to a Nearby Airport

The **NRST** key can be used to find other nearby things. Each time you press it a different type of nearby objects will be displayed.

☑ Press the **NRST** key several times. As you press it, the nearest screen will cycle through the following:

- Airports nearest to your present position.

- Airports nearest to your destination.

- Nearest VORs. The frequency, distance, and bearing of each one is shown.

- Nearest NDBs

- Nearest intersections. This would be useful if ATC asks you to go to an intersection and you're not sure of the spelling, or want to set it up quickly.

- Nearest air traffic control center frequencies.

- Nearest FSS frequencies.

- Nearest user-defined waypoints.

- Nearest airspaces.

You can also use the **Nearest xxxx** line select key to switch between different types of nearest objects. This is the only way to switch on the IFD440, which does not have **NRST** key.

Figure 10 - 23 Displaying Different Types of Nearby Facilities

Utilities

The IFD's UTIL tab contains several useful timers and calculators.

Standard Timers

The standard timers include a generic timer that can be used to time instrument approaches, a trip timer that keeps track of how long you have been flying, and a departure time that records your takeoff time.

For example, you could use the generic timer to time an instrument approach that took one minute and thirty seconds from the final approach fix to the missed approach point. To set this up, do the following:

☑ Press the **AUX** rocker to display the UTIL tab.

☑ Press the **Timers** line select key. The **Timers** page will be displayed.

☑ Tap the on-screen **Down** button in the **Generic Timer** section to select a countdown timer, or place the cursor on **Down** and press the **ENTR** key.

☑ Enter **00:01:30** in the time box. You can do this with the on-screen keyboard or the **IFD Multi-Function** key.

☑ Tap the **Start** button when you cross the final approach fix. The timer will start counting down.

☑ Tap the on-screen **Stop** button to stop the timer at any time. Tap it again to restart it.

☑ Double-tap on the **Reset** button to reset the timer back to its initial value.

☑ Return to the MAP tab to monitor your approach.

Figure 10 - 24 The Timer Page

When the time is up, a **Timer Expired** message will be displayed. You can remove it by pressing the **CLR** key.

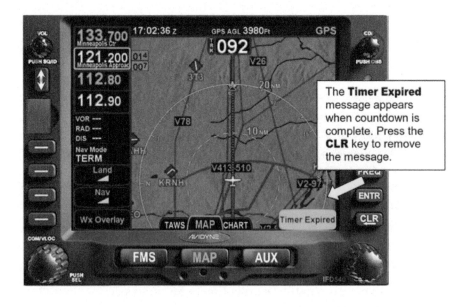

Figure 10 - 25 The Timer Expired Message

The Trip Timer and Event Times timers are similar to each other. Each has two modes: You can choose between starting the time when the IFD is powered up, or when you take off (as determined by GPS groundspeed). Each timer has a reset button. Trip Timer shows the elapsed time since the power-up or takeoff occurred, while Event Times shows the time (in UTC or local time) that the event occurred.

Lesson 10: Information and Utilities

The Flight Timer can be continuously displayed as one of the Datablocks on the MAP page. This is useful if you want to continuously keep track of your time aloft. Datablocks will be explored further in a later chapter.

Custom Timers

In addition to the standard timers, you can define up to ten custom timers of your own choosing. There are three types of custom timers:

1. Event Timers, which count down to a specified date and time. This type of timer could be used to keep track of the due date for an annual inspection.

2. One Time timers, which track the flight time to a specific one-time event.

3. Periodic timers, which also track flight time to an event, but will automatically reset and start timing again after the time is reached. This would be useful for, for example, keeping track of oil changes or 100-hour inspections.

For example, to create a custom timer to track your oil changes do the following:

☑ Press the **AUX** rocker to display the UTIL tab.

☑ Press the **Timers** line select key. The **Timers** page will be displayed.

☑ Use the **IFD Multi-Function** knob to move the **Insert Cursor** under the last timer entry.

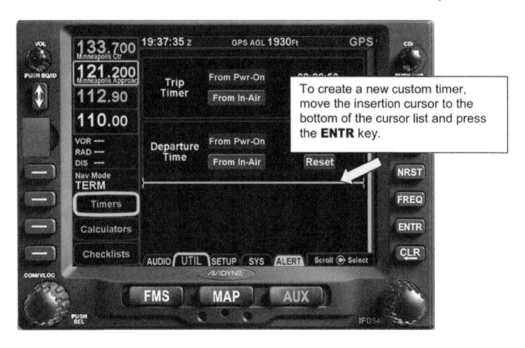

Figure 10 - 26 Positioning the Cursor for a Custom Timer

☑ Press the **ENTR** key. A new custom timer will be created.

☑ Make the following changes to the new custom timer:

   • Change the name of the timer to **Oil Change**.

   • Change the type of the timer to **Periodic**.

   • Change the timer interval to **30.0** flight hours (or use whatever interval is appropriate for your aircraft.)

Lesson 10: Information and Utilities

Figure 10 - 27 Setting Field Values for a Custom Timer

The new timer is now set up. It will count down whenever you are in flight. When the timer has expired an Oil Change message will be displayed on all pages and a yellow Overdue caption will appear on the timer page.

Figure 10 - 28 Custom Timer Message

The Overdue message will remain until you clear it by resetting the counter.

☑ Place the cursor on the **Overdue** box and press the **ENTR** key. The timer will return to its initial value. Since this is a Periodic timer, the timer will start timing again after you reset it.

Lesson 10: Information and Utilities

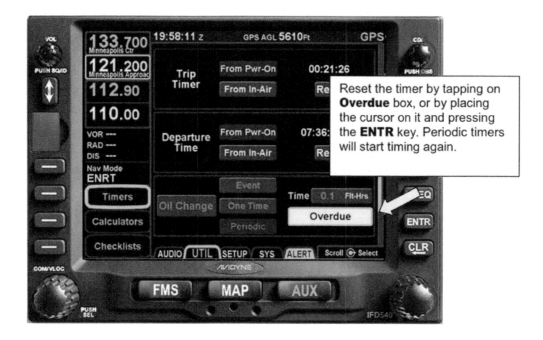

Figure 10 - 29 Resetting a Timer

Calculators

The IFD **Utilities** page also contains several calculators that will solve air data and time-speed-distance problems.

For example, use the calculator to solve the following problem:

- Altitude: 4000 feet
- Outside air temperature 41° F
- Altimeter 29.92
- Calibrated airspeed: 135 knots
- Heading: 080°

What is the true airspeed and the winds aloft?

Do the following:

☑ Press the **AUX** rocker to display the UTIL tab.

☑ Press the **Calculators** line select key. The **Calculators** page will be displayed.

☑ Enter the altitude, airspeed, heading, temperature, and barometer values in the appropriate boxes.

☑ The true airspeed, density altitude, winds aloft, and headwind value will be displayed.

Note: If your IFD is connected to an external sensor, such as an EFIS display, any air data provided by that sensor will automatically populate the appropriate fields. This information will be displayed in green. You can still manually enter data to perform what/if calculations. Press the **CLR** key to erase the manual entries and return to the sensor data.

Figure 10 - 30 Using the Air Data Calculator

Two time-speed-distance calculators are also included: A fuel planner and a trip planner. The fuel planner calculates the fuel required to reach a specified destination. The trip planner calculates the time and distance to a destination. It also shows the estimated time of arrival (ETA) and the time of sunrise/sunset at the destination.

The fuel and trip planners can be used in either of two modes: Present Position and Point-to-Point. Present Position provides information from your present position to any destination airport. Point-to-Point calculates data for any origin-destination pair.

Only airport identifiers can be entered into the Origin or Destination fields.

Note: If an external fuel-flow computer is connected to the IFD, data for the current fuel on board and fuel flow will be entered automatically and will be displayed in green. You can enter your own values if you wish. Press the **CLR** key to return to the fuel computer data.

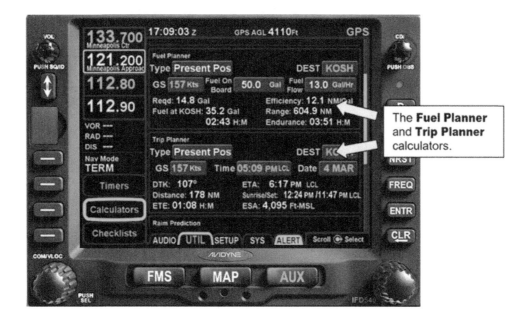

Figure 10 - 31 The Fuel and Trip Planner Calculators

A RAIM (Receiver Autonomous Integrity Monitoring) Prediction calculator and a Trip Statistics calculator are also included. Refer to the IFD Pilot Guide for more information.

AviOS 10.3 adds a Weight Calculator, which provides a means to compute current aircraft weight and to predict landing weight. Basic empty weight, max imum takeoff weight, and maximum landing weight of your specific aircraft are all entered using the Maintenance Mode, typically during installation.

Figure 10 - 31A The Weight Calculator

Electronic Checklists

The IFD can be used to create and execute electronic checklists. Up to nine checklists can be stored. Each check-list can have up to 50 steps, each of which can have up to 30 characters.

Creating an Electronic Checklist

Creating an electronic checklist is done in two steps:

1. Create a directory of named checklists. Usually there is one checklist for each phase of flight. You can have a maximum of nine checklists.

2. Create the contents, or individual steps, of each checklist. A checklist can have up to 50 steps.

Both of these will be explained below.

> **Note:** Creating checklists will be much easier if you use the Avidyne MK10 external keyboard. Checklists can also be created on the IFD540 simulator and uploaded to the IFD in your aircraft. See the Avidyne Pilot Guide for details.

Use the following procedure to create a directory of named checklists:

☑ Use the **AUX** rocker to select the UTIL tab.

☑ Press the **Checklist** line select key. The Checklists directory page will be displayed.

☑ Tap on the **Edit** caption at the top of the page. It will change to display a blue background. This indicates that you are in checklist editing mode.

☑ Use the touch screen or the **IFD Multi-Function** knob to place the cyan cursor box on the checklist name to be entered or edited.

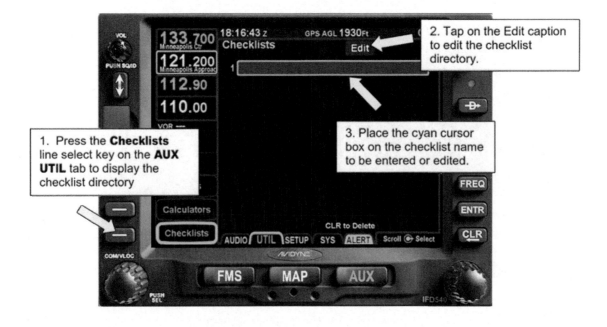

Figure 10 - 32 The Checklist Directory Page

☑ Tap inside the cursor box. The on-screen keyboard will appear. Use it to type in the name of your checklist and tap on the **Enter** button when you're finished.

Figure 10 - 33 Entering a New Checklist Name

☑ Continue this process until all the checklist names have been entered.

☑ When all the checklist names are entered, tap on the **Edit** caption to turn off editing mode. The blue background will disappear.

Figure 10 - 34 Checklist Directory After All Names Have Been Entered

To type in the individual items of a checklist, do the following:

☑ Open the **Checklist** page with the **AUX** rocker switch and the **Checklists** line select key.

☑ Select the checklist you want to edit by tapping on it or turning the **IFD Multi-Function** knob.

☑ Tap on the checklist name again, or press the **ENTR** key. The checklist will open.

☑ Tap on the **Edit** caption at the top of the page. It will turn blue, indicating that the checklist is in editing mode

☑

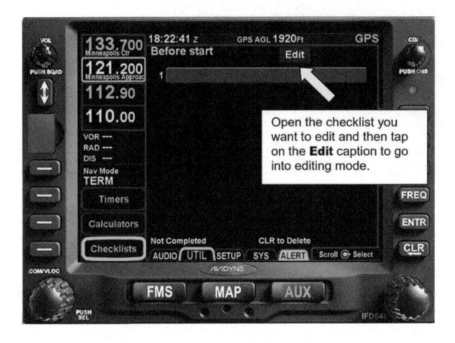

Figure 10 - 35   A New Checklist Before Items Are Entered

☑ If this is a new (empty) checklist, a cyan cursor box will appear around the first checklist item. If it's not a new checklist, tap on the item after the last checklist entry to place the cyan cursor box there.

☑ Tap on the cursor box. The on screen keyboard will be displayed. Use it to enter the text of the checklist item.

☑ Tap the **Enter** button to accept the new checklist item.

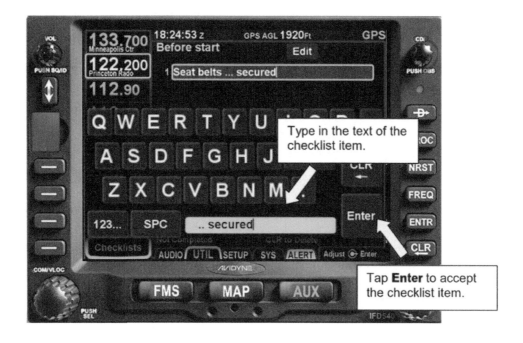

Figure 10 - 36 Checklist Item Entry

☑ Continue entering checklist items until the checklist is complete.

☑ Tap on the **Edit** caption at the top of the screen to turn off checklist editing mode.

☑ Press the **CLR** key to return to the top checklist page.

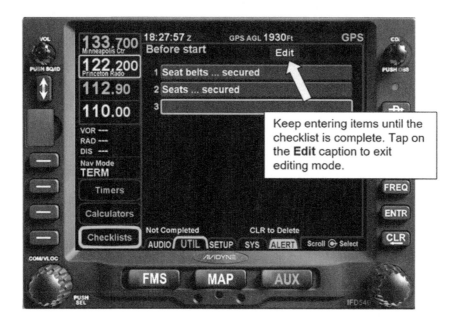

Figure 10 - 37 Checklist After Two Items Have Been Entered

Checklists can be edited in a similar manner. Go to the checklist directory or to the checklist you want to edit, turn on editing mode, and double tap on the item you want to edit. Turn off editing mode when you are finished.

You can move any checklist or checklist entry up or down the list by selecting it in editing mode and then turning the outer **IFD Multi-Function** knob.

A checklist entry or an entire checklist can be erased by selecting it in editing mode and pressing the **CLR** key.

Checklists can be backed up to and retrieved from a USB memory stick. See the Avidyne Pilot Guide for instructions.

Using Electronic Checklists

Follow this procedure to use an electronic checklist (the checklists shown are examples; they will not appear in your simulator unless you create them yourself):

☑ Press the **AUX** rocker to display the UTIL tab.

☑ Press the **Checklists** line select key. The checklist directory will be displayed.

☑ Move the cursor over the checklist you want to use and press the **ENTR** key. The checklist items will be displayed. You can also double-tap on a checklist to select it.

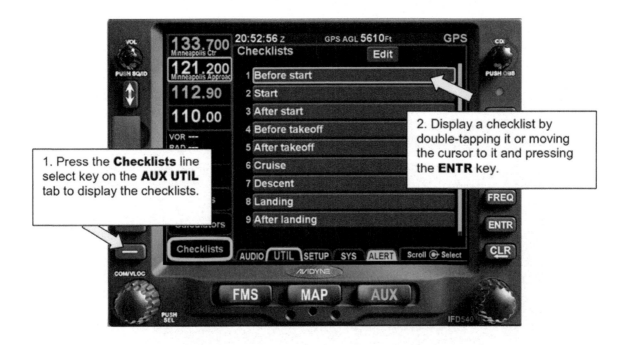

Figure 10 - 38 Displaying the Electronic Checklists

☑ As you accomplish each checklist item, tap on it or move the cursor to it and press the **ENTR** key. The item will turn green and a check mark will appear next to it. The cursor will move automatically to the next item. Or, you can accomplish items out of order by moving the cursor manually.

☑ You can un-check a checked item by tapping on it or moving the cursor to it and pressing the **ENTR** key. The check mark will be removed.

Lesson 10: Information and Utilities

A white **Not Completed** caption is displayed at the bottom of the checklist. This will change to a **Complete** caption when all the items have been accomplished.

Figure 10 - 39 Using an Electronic Checklist

☑   Go back to the list of checklists by pressing the **CLR** key. Checklists that have been started but not finished will be displayed in green with a gray check mark. Completed checklists will have a green check mark.

Figure 10 - 40 A Completed Checklist

To clear all the items in an entire checklist, open the checklist and press the **IFD Multi-Function** knob for about 10 seconds.

System Information

The AUX SYS tab tells you about the software installed in your IFD, the currency of your navigation, obstacle, and chart databases, and the status of you GPS and datalink receivers.

To look at this information, do the following:

Software Version

To see the version of the software installed on your IFD, do the following:

☑ Press the **AUX** rocker to display the SYS tab.

☑ Press the **Status** line select key as necessary to display the **Status Software** caption.

The Software tab will appear, as shown below. The software version number is on the top line.

Figure 10 - 41 Displaying Software Version Information

Navigation, Obstacle, and Chart Databases

The IFD contains separate databases for navigation data, terrain, obstacles, and charts. Each of them must be kept updated with current data from Jeppesen.

To see the status of your databases, do the following:

☑ Press the **AUX** rocker to display the SYS tab.

☑ Press the **Status** line select key as necessary to display the **Status Databases** caption.

The Database Status tab will appear. Valid dates for each type of data are shown.

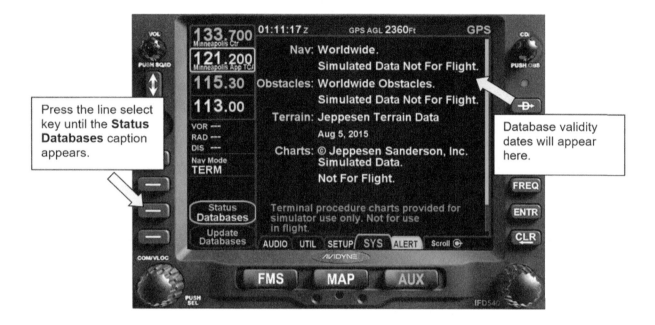

Figure 10 - 42 Displaying Internal Database Information

GPS Status

The GPS Status tab shows the condition of the GPS receiver in your IFD. In particular, it shows whether or not you are receiving WAAS information.

To see the GPS Status tab, do the following:

☑ Press the **AUX** rocker to display the SYS tab.

☑ Press the **Status** line select key as necessary to display the **Status GPS** caption.

The GPS Status tab will appear. The signal level of each GPS satellite appears on the bottom of the screen. The navigation mode and status of SBAS (satellite-based augmentation system – WAAS in the United States) is shown at the top.

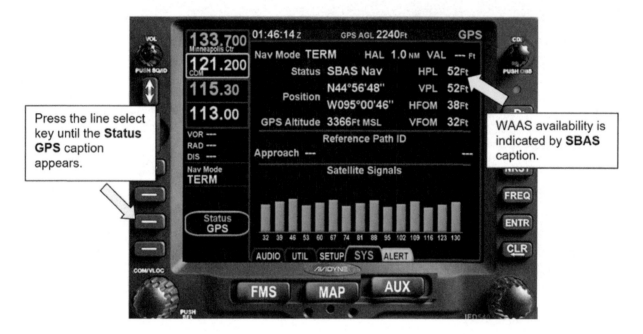

Figure 10 - 43 Displaying Nav Status Information

Datalink Status

The word "Datalink" refers to weather and airspace data from external receivers that can be connected to the IFD. These include Avidyne's MLB100 ADS-B receiver, XM weather receivers, and others.

The status of the information received on datalink is shown on the Datalink Status tab. The exact appearance of this page depends on what type of receiver is connected to your IFD.

To see the Datalink Status tab, do the following:

☑ Press the **AUX** rocker to display the SYS tab.

☑ Press the **Status** line select key as necessary to display the **Status Datalink** caption.

☑ Press the bottom line select key to display the **Datalink Status** caption.

The top of the datalink tab shows the age (in minutes) of the many types of information that are being received. A dash in the age column indicates that no data has been received for the corresponding category.

The bottom of the screen shows the color coding of the weather flags and radar symbols that appear on the MAP page of the IFD.

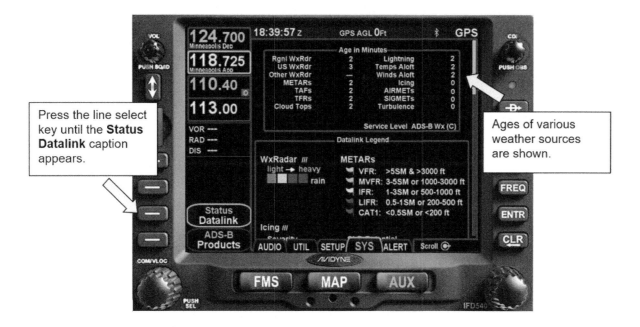

Figure 10 - 44 Displaying Datalink Information

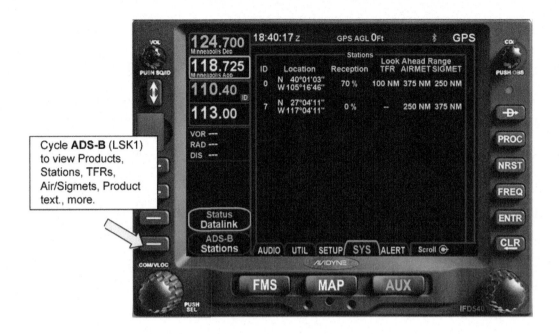

Figure 10 - 45 Displaying Datalink Information

IFD440 and IFD410 Differences

The information sources and utilities that have been explored in this chapter work in the IFD440 and IFD410 as well as the IFD550 and IFD540. There are some differences, however, because the IFD4XX does not have a **NRST** key or a **FREQ** key.

NRST Key

To access the NRST functionality in the IFD4XX, use the **FMS** rocker to display the NRST tab. This brings up the same page that the **NRST** key does.

The different types of nearest objects are accessed by pressing the **Nearest xxxx** line select key, instead of multiple presses of the **NRST** key.

Figure 10 - 46 Displaying the NRST Tab on the IFD440

FREQ Key

The **FREQ** key's information is accessed by turning the lower left COMM/VLOC knob. Once the page is displayed, you can access the individual tabs by tapping on them or turning the outer ring of the right **IFD Multi-Function** knob.

The lower left COMM/VLOC knob is also used for tuning the communications radio, so the FREQ tabs will be displayed whenever you tune a new comm. frequency. Dismiss it by tapping on the red **X** symbol or by pressing the appropriate rocker switch to go back to your previous display.

Figure 10 - 47 Displaying Frequency Information on the IFD440

Lesson Review

This lesson looked at the information and utility features of the Avidyne IFD5XX/4XX. The items that were covered are:

Airport Information

- You can get airport information by using the **FMS** rocker to display the INFO tab.

- The Paste line select key on the INFO tab will contain the identifier of the airport that is currently selected on the **FPL** tab.

- The airport identifier on the INFO tab can be entered manually, or you can use the Paste line select key to paste the identifier of the airport selected on the FPL tab.

- The INFO tab contains a variety of airport information, including general information, communications frequencies, runway information, and other data. Each type of information is in a separate box.

- An INFO box is opened by double-tapping on it or by placing the cursor on it and pressing the ENTR key.

Communications Frequencies

- The INFO tab Communications box contains all the communications frequencies associated with an airport or facility.

- A frequency can be loaded into the standby communications frequency window by tapping on it or by placing the cursor on it and pressing the ENTR key.

Lesson 10: Information and Utilities

- On the IFD540 you can find nearby frequencies by pressing the FREQ key.

- On the IFD440 the FREQ page is displayed by turning the COMM/VLOC frequency selector knob.

- The FREQ page contains departure airport, arrival airport, enroute facility, and recently used frequencies.

Navigation Frequencies

- You can find the frequency of a navigation facility by entering its identifier in the INFO tab.

- The frequency can be pasted into the standby navigation frequency window by tapping on it or by placing the cursor on it and pressing the ENTR key.

Searching for Airports and Facilities

- You can search for a facility by using the Search line select key on the INFO tab.

- Facilities can be searched for by city, state, and type of facility.

Nearby Airports and Facilities

- On the IFD550, IFD540, and IFD525 you can press the NRST key to find nearby facilities.

- On the IFD440 and IFD410 you can use the FPL rocker to bring up the NRST tab. This performs the same function as pressing the NRST key on the IFD5XXs.

- Each press of the NRST key or the NRST line select key displays a different type of nearest facility. The facilities are:

  1. Airports nearest to your current position.

  2. Airports nearest to the destination.

  3. Nearest VORs.

  4. Nearest NDBs.

  5. Nearest intersections.

  6. Nearest air traffic control center frequencies.

  7. Nearest FSS frequencies.

  8. Nearest user-defined waypoints.

  9. Nearest airspaces.

- Nearest items are sorted by distance, closest one first.

- You can go direct to a nearest airport by placing the cursor on it and pressing the Direct key.

- A nearest frequency can be loaded into the standby frequency box by tapping on it or by placing the cursor on it and pressing the ENTR key.

Standard Timers

A list of timers can be displayed by pressing the Timers line select key on the AUX UTIL tab.

Standard timers include:

- A generic timer

- A trip timer

- A departure time timer

- The generic timer can be used to count up or down. It is useful for, among other things, timing instrument approaches.

- A message is displayed when the generic timer runs out.

- The trip timer can be displayed as a Datablock on the MAP page.

Custom Timers

- You can define up to ten custom timers.

- Each custom timer can have its own name.

- A timer can be defined as an event, one time, or periodic timer.

- When the timer expires a message will be displayed and an overdue notice will appear on the Timer page.

- The Overdue notice can be reset by tapping on it or by placing the cursor on it and pressing the ENTR key.

Calculators

- A list of calculators can be displayed by pressing the Calculators line select key on the AUX UTIL tab.

- The calculators include:

- An air data calculator, used to compute true airspeed, density altitude, and winds aloft.

- A fuel planner, used to compute fuel usage requirements.

- A trip calculator, used for time-speed-distance problems.

- A wieght calculator, used computing current weight and predict landing weight.

- A RAIM calculator.

- A trip statistics calculator.

- Any sensors (such as OAT, EFIS/Air Data Computers, or fuel flow computers) attached to the IFD540 will automatically populate appropriate calculator fields. The user can override the automatic entries with manual ones.

- Press the CLR key to erase the manual entries and return to the automatic ones.

Checklists

- The electronic checklist directory page can be displayed by pressing the Checklists line select key on the AUX UTIL tab.

- The IFD can support up to nine separate checklists. Each checklist can have up to 50 steps.

- A checklist is built in two steps:

  1. Add the checklist name to the directory of checklists.

  2. Add the individual checklist items to the checklist.

- The checklist directory or an individual checklist can be edited by tapping on the Edit caption. This puts the checklist in editing mode. Double tap on the Edit caption to leave editing mode.

- Edit a checklist name or an individual checklist item by going to editing mode and then tapping on the name or item. Use the on screen keyboard to enter the new text.

- To use a checklist, double-tap on it or place the cursor on it and pressing the ENTR key.

- When a checklist item has been accomplished, tap on it or place the cursor on it and press the ENTR key. A green check mark will be placed on the item.

- To un-check a completed item, tap on it or place the cursor on it and pressing the ENTR key. The green check mark will be removed.

- Return to the top list of checklists by pressing the CLR key.

- Checklists that have been started but not finished will be displayed in green with gray check marks next to their names. Completed checklists will have green check marks.

- To clear all the items in an entire checklist, open the checklist and press the IFD Multi-Function knob for about 10 seconds.

System Status

- The IFD's software revision status can be found on the AUX→SYS→Status Software tab.

- The navigation, terrain, obstacle, and chart database validity dates are shown on the AUX→SYS→ Status Databases tab.

- The status of WAAS and the GPS receiver appear on the AUX→SYS→Status GPS tab.

- The availability and age of datalink information is shown on the AUX→SYS→Status Datalink tab.

Lesson 11: Pilot Settings and Options

One of the most useful features of the IFD5XX/4XX navigators is that you, the pilot, have a great deal of control over the way your unit behaves and how data is displayed on it. There are dozens of settings and options that can be used to configure the IFDs to your liking. They include controls to manage which features are displayed on the MAP page, what navigation data appears on the screen, how the lighting is controlled, what elements are used in flight plans, and many others.

This lesson will introduce you to many of the Setup options of the IFD. It is only an introduction; there are far too many options to explain each one of them in detail. Instead, this lesson will show you a few useful settings and how to configure them. Avidyne's IFD Pilot Guides contain a full explanation of every option. Refer to them for more detail.

At the end of this lesson you will understand how the Setup pages work and what kind of options can be found on them. You will know how to control every option and how to find its definition in the Avidyne Pilot Guide.

Saving and Retrieving Settings for Individual Users

As you will soon see, there are many pilot-controlled settings. Getting them all configured for your liking can be a daunting task, involving lots of tweaking. But what if you share an airplane with another pilot? His or her preference may be different than yours. His or her tweaks will destroy all of your tweaks, and vice-versa. That leaves no one happy.

Fortunately, the IFD includes the capability of storing "user settings." This means that up to **TEN** individual users can save and retrieve their own set of user preference profiles. You can set things the way you want, save them, and retrieve them when you return to the airplane. Your changes will not affect the settings of the other pilots, nor will theirs affect yours.

With AviOS 10.3 and newer, all Alerts, Charts, Connectivity, Datablocks, Display, FMS, Map, Radio, Terrain, Time, Units and User Profile options have been combined onto this single Setup Tab page. The Setup page is organized using a set of categories and each category can be expanded to reveal settings relevant to that category. Only one category can be expanded and/or edited at a time, therefore, when one category is expanded, all other categories at that same level are condensed. In this chapter we will cover some of the more pertinent Setup functions but not all of them. Please refer to the IFD Pilot's Guide for additional information on any specific Setup function.

User Profiles

To access your own settings, do the following:

- ☑ Press the **AUX** rocker to display the **SETUP** tab.

- ☑ Use the touch screen or the outer **IFD Multi-Function** knob to put the cursor on the **User Profile** category, which is all the way at the bottom of the page.

- ☑ There are ten possible user profiles. Use Line Select Key (LSK 3) **User** button to change the active user to the one you want.

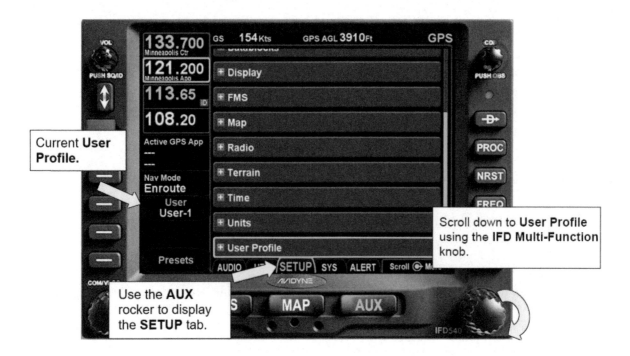

Figure 11 - 1 Setting up a User Profile

Setting a User Name

The default User name provided by the Avidyne factory is "User-1" for User Name 1. You will notice User Name 2 through User Name 10 do not have names assigned, which means there is only one set of user settings defined at this time. To add additional profiles, simply add a name next to User Name 2 such as "User 2" and User Name 3 to "User 3," etc.   However, these are not particularly informative and it would be better to set your own user names, like "Neil," "Buzz," and "Mike."

Fortunately, there is a way to do this. To make a customized user name, do the following:

- ☑ Press the **AUX** rocker to display the SETUP tab.

- ☑ Scroll down to the bottom of the page and select and expand the **User Profiles** category.

- ☑ Use the touch screen or the right outer **IFD Multi-Function** knob to put the cursor on the **User Name 1** line,

- ☑ Push the right inner **IFD Multi-Function** knob to select and edit using the inner and outer right knobs

- ☑ Or simply touch the highlighted field to bring up an on-screen keyboard to change the active user to the user profile you want to change.

- ☑ Press the **ENTR** key to save the new name.

You will notice when you assign more than one User Name, a **User** line select key will be visible at LSK 3 position with the Name assigned for the currently selected User Profile. This LSK will allow you to easily switch between all defined user profiles. If you only have two user profiles defined, pushing the User LSK will toggle between the two. If you have three or more then the User LSK will cycle through each of them in order and then repeat. Any new User Profiles created will have the factory default settings, which can then easily be edited.

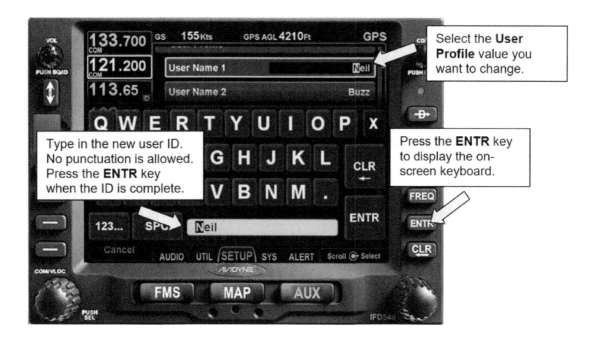

Figure 11 - 2 Setting a New User Profile

Datablocks and How to Use Them

One of the more useful features of the IFD is the fact that the pilot can set up "Datablocks" which are displayed on the primary MAP page in flight. As its name implies, a datablock is box which contains an item of flight data. There are a large number of different things that can be displayed, all of which may or may not be useful to you. Which ones you want to see will depend on your own preferences. You can also see none at all, if you prefer a clean, uncluttered look for your IFD.

Datablocks appear on the left side, on the top, and on the right side of the IFD5XX's MAP display. The left and top datablocks are fixed in place, but the ones on the right can be scrolled up and down, so you can have roughly twice as many datablocks as can be seen at one time. You can hide or display the right datablocks by tapping on the vertical MAP tab next to the datablocks.

Datablocks are placed in "slots;" each piece of information occupies at least one slot. There are nine datablock slots in the left-side group, two in the top group and 30 in the right group. Most datablocks are more than one slot tall, and a few take as many as five slots, so the number that can be seen at any one time will depend on which datablocks you choose to display in which place. Since the top datablock space is only one line tall, only single-slot datablocks are available in those two spaces. Only valid options will be presented when setting up each specific datablock.

The smaller display of the IFD4XX does not allow room for left-side datablocks. The IFD4XX will also require more scrolling to view all of the right-side data blocks, since fewer will be visible at the same time.

Every IFD comes from the factory configured with a default set of datablocks. But these are only a starting point. You can change the datablocks to show whatever information you want. And, if you don't like what you've done you can easily go back to the factory settings and start over again.

Datablocks are one of the items controlled by the user profile setting discussed in the previous section of this lesson. Each pilot who flies your airplane can configure their own set of datablocks. Their configuration will be restored whenever they brings up their own user profile.

A single piece of flight information can be displayed in multiple datablocks, so you could use the scrolling feature of the right datablocks to set up several groups of datablocks, each of which could be displayed during a different phase of flight. For example, you could have one set of right datablocks to be displayed in cruise flight, and another below it to be displayed during an approach. When you start your approach you could simply scroll the right datablocks down using the touch screen to hide the cruise entries and display the approach entries. This would be especially useful on the IFD440, where screen space is very limited.

The secret to using datablocks successfully is to keep them the same on every flight. Then you'll know exactly where each piece of information is and how to find it quickly. If you spend a little time designing your setup you won't need to change it once you find a configuration that works best for you.

Figure 11 - 3 IFD540 Datablock Locations

Setting up your own Datablocks

Let's perform an exercise with the IFD540 simulator to see how the datablocks can be configured. In the exercise you will:

1. Clear out all the factory datablocks to start with a completely blank configuration.

2. Set up a suggested set of datablocks, which you can modify as you see fit.

3. Return to the factory configuration.

Start the exercise by doing the following:

- ☑ Start the IFD540 simulator.

- ☑ Go to the ROUTE tab and activate the **OSH AIRVENTURE** flight plan you built in a previous lesson. (You don't need a current flight plan to work with datablocks, but having one will make them easier to understand.)

- ☑ Press the **AUX** rocker to display the **SETUP** tab.

- ☑ Select the **Presets** line select key (Fig 11-4)

- ☑ Highlight the **Datablocks** category from the list of Setup items.

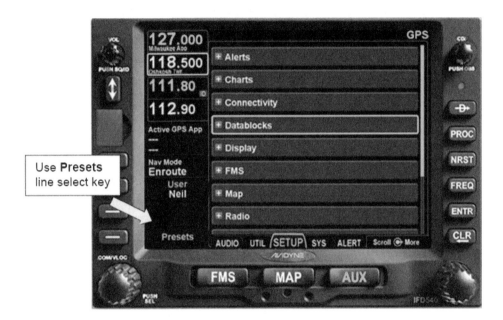

Figure 11 - 4 Selecting the Custom Datablocks

Clear the Old Datablocks

Before you set up your new datablocks it is useful to clear out all the ones set by the factory. This is an **optional step** – there's no requirement that the old datablocks be cleared before you set up new ones. But if you start with a blank slate it will be easier to see what you're doing and how your new datablocks fit together.

The exercise's new configuration will only affect the top and right datablocks. (You will leave the left ones in the factory setting.) So you'll only clear the top and right datablocks.

Use this procedure:

- ☑ Press the **Presets** line select key (LSK1) to display the **Datablock Presets,** Map Details Presents, and All Factory Settings menu items.

- ☑ Open the **Datablock Presets** menu and select **Custom Settings**, then **Enter** . (Fig 11-5.

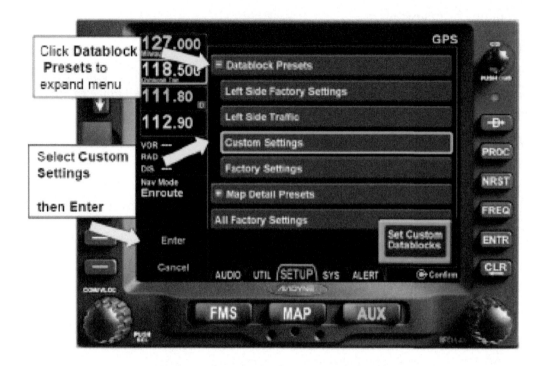

Figure 11 - 5 Selecting a Datablock to Edit

☑ Use the touch screen or the inner **IFD Multi-Function** knob to scroll to the top left data block. Place the cursor on the ***Blank*** entry. This sets the datablock you have selected (the top left one) to blank.

Figure 11 - 6 Setting a Datablock to Blank

☑ Place the cursor on the right top datablock in the top group. Use the same procedure to scroll down the list of options and place the cursor on the ***Blank*** entry.

☑ The top right datablock is now set to blank.

☑ Place the cursor on the top datablock in the right-side group. Set it to *****Blank***** as you did the other two.

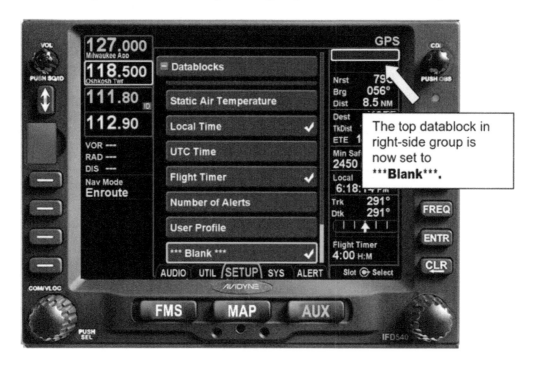

Figure 11 - 7 Another Datablock Set to Blank

☑ Move down all the right-side datablocks, selecting each one and setting it to blank.

☑ When you are finished, the left-side datablocks should still be set to the factory's values. The top and right datablocks should be all blank.

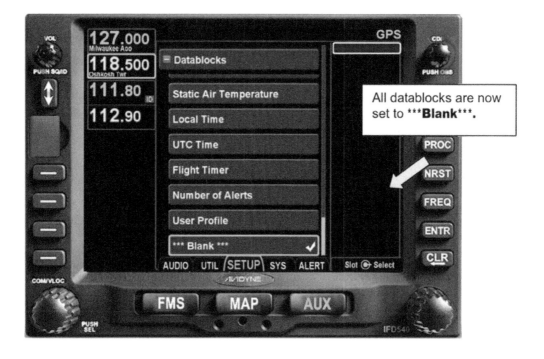

Figure 11 - 8 All Datablocks Set to Blank

Set the New Datablocks

Now that the datablocks are all blank, you're ready to set up your own customized ones. This exercise will demonstrate one possible configuration. It is completely optional – you can change it to whatever makes the most sense to you.

The datablocks shown here were chosen to enhance your situational awareness. That is, they will display where you are, where you're going, what's going to happen next, and what your fuel status is. The suggested datablocks you will set up are:

Top Block:

- Minimum Safe Altitude – to give you awareness of the terrain.

- Flight Timer – to indicate how much time and fuel you've used.

Right Block:

- Nearest Airport – to give you an emergency destination.

- To Waypoint Information – to show where you're going now and when you'll get there.

- Destination Along Track Information – to show total distance and time to your destination.

- Ground Speed – to show how fast you're going.

- UTC Time – so you know what time it is in ATC's world.

- GPS CDI – to show your current and desired tracks. If you set your heading to make these the same you will parallel your programmed course line.

- Active GPS Approach – to confirm the approach you're flying. (This is at the bottom of the right datablock stack. Scroll up to see it during the approach phase.)

> **Note:** If you have a fuel computer connected to your IFD the waypoint and destination datablocks will show projected fuel on board as well as distance and ETA.

Left Block (same as factory settings):

- Decoded VLOC IDENT

- Navigation Mode

Let's get started on setting these up. Do the following:

- ☑ Tap on the left datablock in the top group.

- ☑ Use the touch screen or the inner **IFD Multi-Function** knob to scroll up the **Top Block Options** screen and place the cursor on the **Minimum Safe Altitude** entry. This sets the top left datablock to display the MSA.

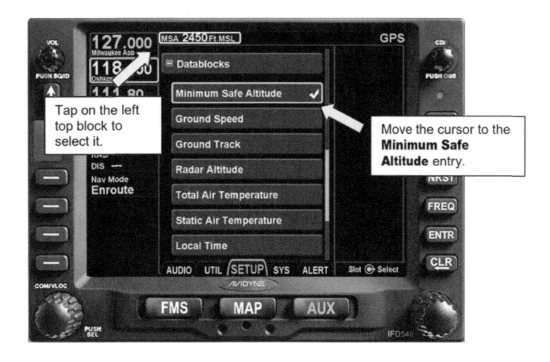

Figure 11 - 9 Setting a New Datablock Value

☑ Select the right datablock in the top group. Scroll down to the **Flight Timer** entry and place the cursor on it.

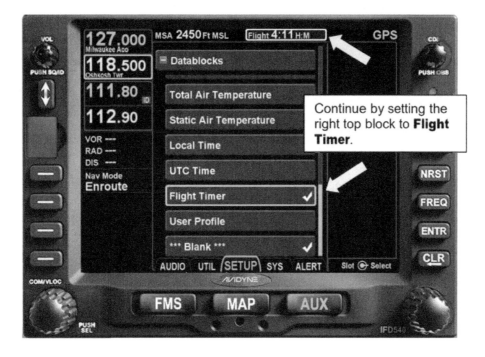

Figure 11 - 10 Setting the Next Datablock Value

☑ Select the top entry in the right datablock group. Set it to **Nearest Airport**.

☑ Continue with the other datablocks in the right group. As you move down the stack, set them to:

• To Waypoint Information

- Destination Along Track Info

- Ground Speed

- UTC Time

- GPS CDI

- Active GPS Approach.

When you are finished the datablocks will be set up in the suggested configuration. The next figure shows how they would look during a GPS approach. Note that the Active GPS Approach datablock is barely visible. You could scroll it up during an approach, which would hide the Nearest Airport datablock. You probably already know where the nearest airport is – it's the one where you're landing.

Figure 11 - 11 Completed Datablocks

Using Datablocks to Display Multiple Standby Radio Frequencies (IFD5XX Only)

In its factory configuration the IFD5XX will display only one standby communications frequency and one standby navigation frequency. However, you can use the datablock feature to display up to four standby frequencies, both communication and navigation. This would be useful, for example, if you were patrolling the highways in a small area and wanted lots of frequencies available for instant use.

The additonal standby frequencies will occupy space in the left datablock area. They take the place of the navigation ID and mode datablocks that appear there in the factory default configuration.

To set up multiple standby frequencies, do the following:

☑ Bring up the **AUX -->Setup-->Datablocks** category as described earlier.

☑ Use the outer **IFD Multi-Function** knob to move the datablock cursor to the navigation radio frequency blocks, just below the two communication frequencies. In the factory configuration this will be the **VLOC Radio** datablock.

Note: You must use the outer IFD Multi-Function knob to select this datablock. You can't use the touch screen. When you tap here on the screen the IFD thinks you're trying to change the standby radio frequency and it pops up the on-screen numeric keyboard.

Figure 11 - 12 Selecting the Top Left Datablock

☑   Move the cursor on the **Left Block Options** list to the **COMM/VLOC Standby #2** entry.

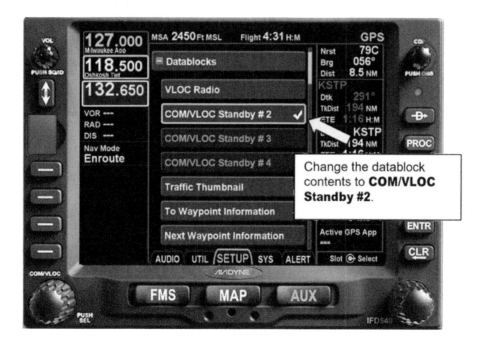

Figure 11 - 13 Changing the Top Left Datablock to a Standby Com Frequency

Lesson 11: Pilot Settings and Options

☑ Use the touch screen or the **IFD Multi-Function** knob to select the next slot in the left datablock group. This is the **Decoded VLOC IDENT** datablock in the factory configuration.

☑ Change this datablock to **COMM/VLOC Standby #3.**

☑ Use the same procedure to change the next datablock to **COMM/VLOC Standby #4.**

☑ There's one more datablock slot in the left group. Set it to **Navigation Mode** to mimic the factory setting. (The decoded VLOC entry might be better, but it won't fit.)

Your IFD is now equipped with four standby frequencies. To use any one of them, place the cursor on it by tapping on it, then select the frequency you want with the COMM/VLOC knob or the on-screen keyboard. Activate the new frequency by pressing the Frequency Swap key. The cyan box indicates which standby block is being accessed and can flip to the active frequency, but only the first standby frequency (the one immediately below the active frequency) will output "standby monitor" audio to an audio panel. The standby audio does not change or correspond to the cyan box.

These boxes normally display standby communication, not navigation, frequencies. Press the COM/VLOC knob to change the boxes to navigation frequencies. They can be set and used in the same way as the communications frequencies.

Figure 11 - 14 IFD540 Set Up with Four Standby Frequencies

Returning to the Factory's Default Datablocks

You can alternate between your custom datablocks settings and the factory defaults. Do the following:

☑ Use the **AUX** rocker to select the SETUP tab.

☑ Press the **Presets** line select key to display use the **Enter** key (or touch screen) to expand the **Datablock Presets** category .

☑ Place the cursor on the **Factory Settings** option.

Lesson 11: Pilot Settings and Options

This will return all the datablocks to the factory settings, but your custom settings will re-appear if you move the cursor back down to the Custom option.

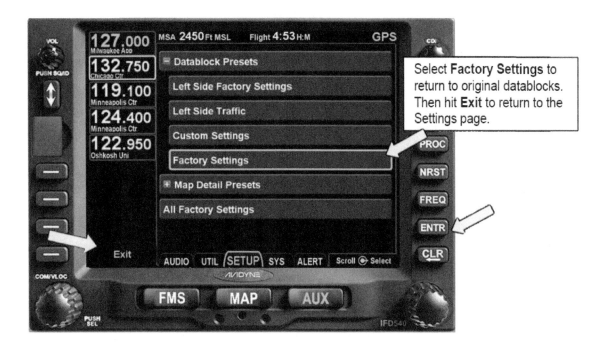

Figure 11 - 15 Returning to the Factory Default Datablocks

If you want to erase all your custom settings you must perform another few steps:

- ☑ With the **Factory Settings** option selected (as shown above), press the **Enter** key to approve the change.

- ☑ Press the **Exit** line select key to go back to the **Settings** page.

- ☑ You can bring up your **Custom** settings again any time you choose, or you can edit them as you see fit.

FMS Setup

The FMS Setup page is used to tailor the operation of the internal flight management system for the type of flying you do. You can set your preferred descent rate, what kind of airspace alerts you'll see, and what kind of airways and procedures you can select. For example, if you're a VFR-only pilot you can turn off all the departures, arrivals, approaches, and high altitude airways. You will never be prompted to select any of them.

The FMS options in use are controlled by the user profile setting. Each pilot can configure the FMS in his or her own way and retrieve his or her settings when it's his or her turn to fly.

For the purposes of this exercise, let's say that you are an IFR pilot who flies at altitudes below 18,000 feet. You always fly on an IFR flight plan, so you don't want to be bothered with controlled airspace alerts. You never use high altitude airways, so you don't want to see them in the "choice" boxes.

Turning off Controlled Airspace Alerts

To turn off alerts for controlled airspace, do the following:

- ☑ Use the **AUX** rocker to select the SETUP tab.

- ☑ Press the **Setup** line select key to display the **SETUP** FMS caption.

- ☑ Use the touch screen or the outer **IFD Multi-Function** knob to highlight the **Controlled Airspace** field.

- ☑ Use the inner **IFD Multi-Function** knob to change the field's value to **Off**.

Alerts will no longer be displayed when you are nearing controlled airspace.

Figure 11 - 16 Controlling Airspace Alerts

Turning off High Altitude Airways

To prevent high altitude airways from being offered as a choice when you are building a flight plan, do the following:

- ☑ Display the **Setup FMS** page, as described above.

- ☑ Use the touch screen or the outer **IFD Multi-Function** knob to highlight the **High Altitude Airways** field.

- ☑ Use the inner **IFD Multi-Function** knob to change the field's value to **Off**.

Figure 11 - 17 Turning Off Jet Airway Display

Approach Settings

As was explained in Lesson 9, there are several user settings that affect the way that instrument approaches are performed. Two of these settings relate to the FMS and the other two relate to the NAV Radio (and do not apply when using the IFD545, IFD510, and IFD410). The default settings/ recommended values are as follows:

AUX-> SETUP-> FMS

- Advisory Glideslope – On

- Auto Enable Missed – On

AUX-> SETUP-> RADIO

- Auto VLOC Tuning – On

- GPS → VLOC Capture – Auto

-

To change these settings:

☑ Use the **AUX** rocker to select the SETUP tab.

☑ Use the touch screen or the right **IFD Multi-Function** knob to place select and expand the **FMS** or **Radio** category.

☑ For the FMS, move the cursor down to the **Advisory Glideslope** line and/or the **Auto Enable Missed** line

☑ Push in on the right inner **IFD Multi-Function** knob, which changes the field to white background, meaning it is editable. Twist the inner **IFD Multi-Function** knob to change to "On" or "Off" as desired.

Figure 11 - 18 The Approach Settings - FMS related

Figure 11 - 19 The Approach Settings - NAV Radio-related

Visual Approach Settings

As was explained in Lesson 9 regarding Visual Approaches, there are several user settings that affect the way that visual approaches are displayed. From the AUX->Setup->FMS menu, you are able to customize the parameters of your Visual Approach pattern, including Leg length, Pattern Width, and Glideslope angle.

Figure 11 - 20 Visual Approach Settings

If you are not given the option to select Visual Approaches in the pull down menu when you select a PROC, make sure the Visual Approaches option is "On" from the AUX->Setup->FMS page, and the following settings are as you want them:

Final Length - This setting allows you to to set the length of the final approach, as depicted on the map display when showing a visual approach with either a base or downwind entry. The default setting is 1.0nm. Can be set to .5nm minimum to 10.0nm maximum

Pattern Width - This setting controls the pattern width of the visual approach (i.e. the length of the base leg) when showing a visual approach with either a base or a downwind entry. The factory default setting is 1.2 nautical miles. Can be set to .5nm minimum to 9.9nm maximum

Glideslope - This setting controls the glideslope angle used to generate advisory vertical guidance on a visual approach. The factory default setting is 4.0 degrees, but can be set from 3º to 5º in 1/10th degree increments.

To change any of these settings:

☑ Use the **AUX** rocker to select the SETUP tab.

☑ Use the touch screen or the right **IFD Multi-Function** knob to highlight and expand the **FMS** category.

☑ Move the cursor down to the **Visual Approaches** line.

☑ Push in on the right inner **IFD Multi-Function** knob to any of the available settings, which changes the field to white background, meaning it is editable. Twist the inner **IFD Multi-Function** knob to edit as desired.

VNAV Settings

The IFD is capable of providing vertical navigation during descent operations when several conditions are met, including receiving valid baro-corrected altitude. Your VNAV descent path is defined by the altitude constraints in the flight plan and also the descent angle specified on the AUX->Setup->FMS page. When enroute VNAV is active, the IFD will provide vertical deviations to the descent path. The enroute VNAV capability must be enabled by the installer after it is determined that the aircraft is equipped to perform the function.

Figure 11 - 21 VNAV Settings

As explained in the IFD Pilot's Guide, if enroute VNAV is not allowed, enroute vertical deviations will not be generated. However, the IFD will still compute the top-of-descent (TOD) point using VNAV descent angle or rate.

For VNAV operations the user can select how the decent path is defined with the following settings:.

Path Basis - This setting allows you to switch between Descent Angle and Descent Rate.

Descent Angle/Descent Rate - This setting will change based on the previous setting. Descent angle can be user-selectable from 1º - 6º and Descent Rate, which has a default is 500fpm, can be set from 50fpm - 2,000fpm.

Map Setup

You can customize the moving map screen to display only the features you want to see. This can be done to simplify the map by eliminating things that do not interest you. The map settings in use are controlled by the user profile setting; each pilot who flies your airplane can display his or her own favorite map features.

Airport Filter

The Airport Filter is used to control the display of airports on the map and to control which airports appear when you press the Nearest key. You can select all airports, or you can filter them by runway length, whether they have a control tower, the type of runway surface, and the availability of fuel.

For this exercise you will set the airport filter to display only airports with hard surface runways which are over 3500 feet long.

Do the following:

☑ Use the **AUX** rocker to select the SETUP tab.

☑ Press the **Setup** line select key to display the **SETUP MAP** caption.

☑ Use the outer **IFD Multi-Function** knob to place the cursor on the **Runway Length** line.

☑ Use the inner **IFD Multi-Function** knob to change the field's value to >3500 FT. (The knob does not "wrap" as it goes through the settings. If you turn it and it does nothing, turn it the other way.)

☑ Move the cursor to the **Runway Surface** field.

☑ Use the inner **IFD Multi-Function** knob to change the field's value to **Hard**.

Your IFD will now only find and display airports with hard surface runways at least 4000 feet long.

Note: If you want to be able to find both hard and soft surface runways, you should change the filter setting to **Hard/Soft**. The default setting of "**Any**" will include water runways. This could have some unexpected consequences if you are not flying a seaplane.

Figure 11 - 22 Setting Runway Filters

Note: When you display the **NRST** page you can always turn off the filter and display all airports by pressing the **Filter** line select key.

Figure 11 - 23 Turning the Runway Filter On and Off

Map Feature Presets

The user of the IFD has complete control of the features which are shown on the moving map. Each type of feature can be turned on or off completely, or it can be set to be displayed at a specified zoom value, altitude, or any of the three settings under the **Nav** decluttering line select key on the MAP page.

The display of map detail is controlled through the Map Detail Default parameter in the Map General box. This setting has four possible values:

1. Factory – The factory default settings

2. IFR – The map is optimized for IFR operations.

3. VFR – The map is optimized for VFR operations.

4. Custom – Custom settings are used, as configured in the Map Detail box.

Each type of map feature can be controlled individually in the Map Detail box. Usually you won't want to deal with that level of detail. A good shorthand method of controlling the features is to use the VFR or IFR setting. Each setting displays map features that are appropriate to that type of operation.

For example, to set the moving map for IFR flying, do the following:

☑ Use the **AUX** rocker to select the SETUP tab.

☑ Press the **Setup** line select key to display the **SETUP MAP** caption.

☑ Use the outer **IFD Multi-Function** knob to place the cursor on the **Map Detail Default** line.

☑ Use the inner **IFD Multi-Function** knob to change the field's value to **IFR**.

As you change the value of the Map Detail Default field you can see the individual values in the Map Detail box changing. That's how you can see the differences between Factory, IFR, and VFR modes. To reset your IFD Map settings for IFR, select the Presets line select key on the **AUX->Setup** page, highlight the IFR Settings Settings under Map Detail Presets, and press the **ENTR** key to complete the reset.

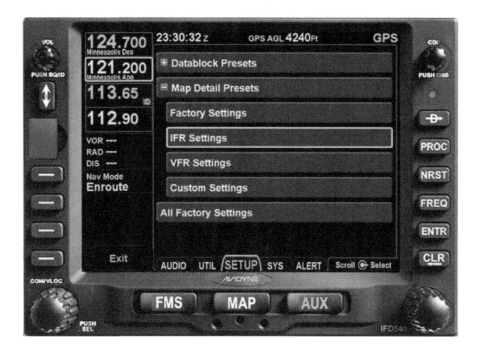

Figure 11 - 24 Map detail Presets - IFR Settings

You can also customize your Map detail settings. In this example we enable the display of Compass Rose on the Map, which was previously off. Go to the **AUX->Setup** tab, under the Map category, highlight Compass Ross, inner **IFD Multi-Function** knob to change the field to white background, twist the knob to change from Off to On, then push the knob again.

Figure 11 - 25 Customizing the Display of Map Features

Returning to the Factory Default Map Settings

To return to the factory default Map settings select the Presets line select key on the **AUX->Setup** page, highlight the Factory Settings under Map Detail Presets, and press the **ENTR** key to complete the reset.

Figure 11 - 26 SMap Detail Presents - Factory Settings

Alerts Setup

The Alerts category in the **AUX->Setup** page allows you to control the various visual and aural alert options of the IFD corresponding to different events. For this exercise, we will set the Switch Tanks alert. All other alert functions have similar knob and button operations to enable/disable. Refer to the IFD Pilot's Guide for all the details on other Alerts.

Setting the Switch Tanks Alert

The IFD contains a Switch Tanks Alert feature that can be used to remind you to change fuel tanks at a specified interval. This can be handy if you are flying an airplane that can only feed from one tank at a time. When the time is up, a Switch Tanks alert will be displayed and the timer will automatically restart its countdown.

Use this procedure to set the timer:

- ☑ Use the **AUX** rocker to select the SETUP tab.

- ☑ Use the touch screen or the right **IFD Multi-Function** knob to place select and expand the **Alerts** category.

- ☑ Move the cursor on the **Switch Tanks Alert** line.

- ☑ Push in on the right inner **IFD Multi-Function** knob, which changes the field to white background, meaning it is editable. Twist the inner **IFD Multi-Function** knob to set the time to the desired interval. The interval can be set in 15 minute increments for up to an hour.

☑ Push the **IFD Multi-Function** knob again or use the Enter key to accept the change. The background of the field will change back to cyan color.

☑ To turn the switch tanks alert off, set the interval to **Never**.

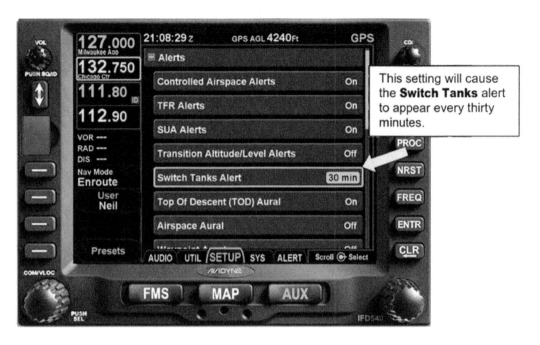

Figure 11 - 27 Setting the Switch Tanks Alert

Waypoint Aural Alert

AviOS10.3 and later softare adds another nice feature with the Waypoint Aler. When enabled, this setting controls whether the IFD will generate an aural message as waypoints in the flight plan are sequenced.

- If the waypoint being sequenced is the final approach fix, the aural is "Final Approach".

- If the waypoint being sequenced is the missed approach point, the aural is "Missed Approach".

- For all other waypoints, the aural is "Waypoint"

The factory default setting is "On" but in case you need to disable or enable the setting:

☑ Use the **AUX** rocker to select the SETUP tab.

☑ Use the touch screen or the right **IFD Multi-Function** knob to place select and expand the **Alerts** category.

☑ Move the cursor on the **Waypoint Aural** line.

☑ Push in on the right inner **IFD Multi-Function** knob, which changes the field to white background, meaning it is editable. Twist the inner **IFD Multi-Function** knob to change to "On" or "Off" as desired.

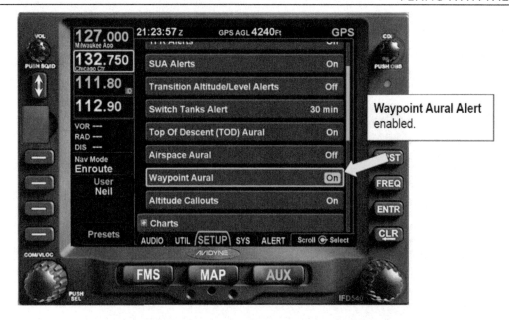

Figure 11 - 28 Setting the Waypoint Aural Alert

Time Setup

Setting the Local Time Format

The first option in this exercise controls the way that the current local time is displayed. The factory default is to display it in 12 hour format. You can change this to 24 hour or UTC format. Today you will change it to 24 hour display.

Figure 11 - 29 Setup Page - Time setup

Do the following:

- ☑ Use the **AUX** rocker to select the SETUP tab.

- ☑ Use the touch screen or the right **IFD Multi-Function** knob to scroll down to the **Time** category, which expands oout to sjpw UTC, Local Time Offset, time Format, and Local Time

- ☑ Use the touch screen or the **IFD Multi-Function** knob to place the cursor on the **Time Format** line.

Figure 11 - 30 Selecting the Time Format Line

- ☑ Use the inner **IFD Multi-Function** knob to move the cursor down to the Time Format line, push in on the **IFD Multi-Function** knob and you field will turn white. Twist the knob to change the time format to **24 Hr**. (You will also have the option for UTC time). Push the knob again and the field will turn cyan. The time shown in the **Current Time** field (just below) will change to the new format. You can also perform this function using the touch screen.

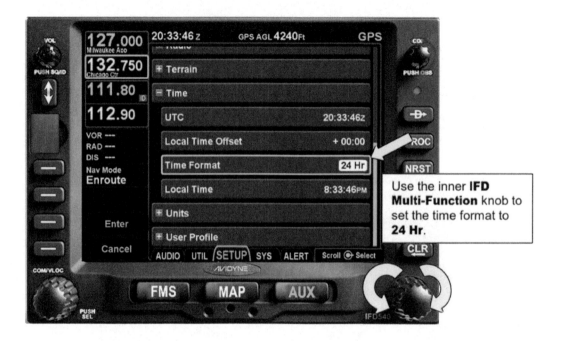

Figure 11 - 31 Changing the Time Format Setting

Note: The Time Format field affects the display of the local time. In order for the local time to be correct, you must also place the appropriate value in the Local Time Offset field. See the **Aux Subsystem** chapter of the IFD Pilot Guide for details.

Communication Frequency Presets

The IFD can store up to sixteen "preset" communications frequencies. These are useful if you use the same frequencies often and want to have them readily available. If you wire an optional switch to your IFD you can control the selection of the preset frequencies from your control yoke, giving you the ability to tune your radio without ever touching it. See the IFD Pilot Guide and the Installation Manual for details.

Setting the Communications Presets

Let's set the Oshkosh tower and ATIS frequencies, 118.50 and 125.90, as the first two communications presets. Do the following:

- ☑ Use the **AUX** rocker to select the AUDIO tab.

- ☑ Press the **Com Preset List** line select key. The communications presets will be displayed.

Figure 11 - 32 The Communications Frequency Preset Page

☑ Tap on the **Edit** button on the communications preset screen. It will turn blue, indicating that you are now in Edit mode.

☑ Tap on the first communications preset box. A cyan cursor will appear around it.

☑ Tap on the box again. An on-screen keyboard will pop up. Type in the frequency 118.50. (You can also set the frequency with the **IFD Multi-Function** knob, if you wish.)

☑ Press the ENTR button. This will save the frequency and exit the Edit mode.

> **Note:** When you type in a communications preset frequency you must enter the **entire** number, including the decimal point. This is different from other places where you enter frequencies.

☑ Use the same procedure to enter the frequency 129.50 in the second preset position.

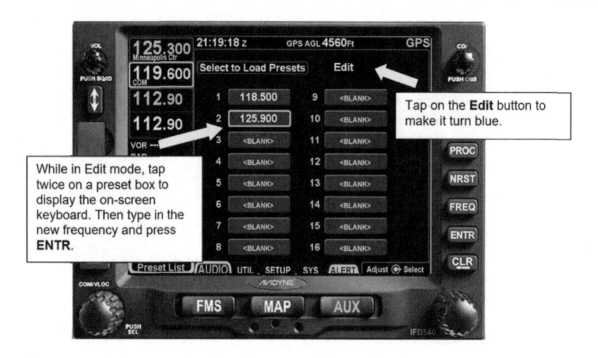

Figure 11 - 33 Setting a Communications Frequency Preset

Using a Communications Preset Frequency

To use an existing communications preset frequency (without the optional yoke switch), follow this procedure:

☑ Use the **AUX** rocker to select the AUDIO tab.

☑ Press the **Com Preset List** line select key.

☑ Tap on the desired frequency, or select it with the **IFD Multi-Function** knob and press the **ENTR** key. The frequency is now loaded in the standby communications frequency box. A small triangle will appear next to the preset frequency box, indicating that it is in use.

☑ Press the **Frequency Swap** key to activate the selected frequency.

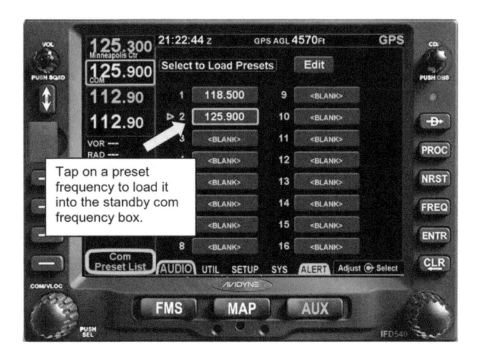

Figure 11 - 34 Loading a Preset Communications Frequency

Deleting a Communications Preset Frequency

Use these steps to delete a preset frequency:

☑ Use the **AUX** rocker to select the AUDIO tab.

☑ Press the **Com Preset List** line select key.

☑ Tap on the **Edit** button. It will turn blue.

☑ Tap on the desired frequency, or select it with the inner **IFD Multi-Function** knob.

☑ Press the **CLR** key.

☑ Tap on the **Edit** button again. It will no longer be blue. The frequency will be replaced by **<BLANK>**.

Connectivity Setup

To enable Bluetooth and WiFi capabilities of the IFD, go to the AUX->SETUP page. Double click on Connectivity to view its available settings. When first expanded, the connectivity category will contain high level items as illustrated below. Scroll the cursor down or simply touch the WiFi line and double click to toggle ON/OFF settings

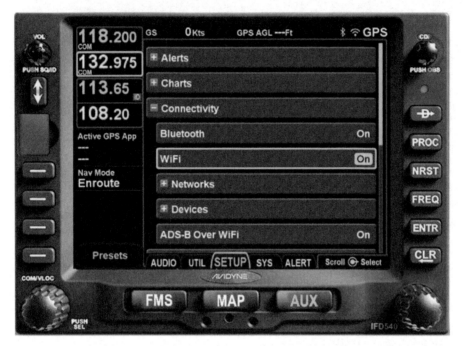

Figure 11 - 35 Connectivity - Turning on Bluetooth & WiFi

Scroll down or touch to move the cursor over Networks. Double click or hit ENTR key to expand Networks menu. All available networks weill be listed here. In this case we have the IFD's default network name which is its serial number.   Please refer to the IFD Pilot's Guide for editing of IFD network name and password.

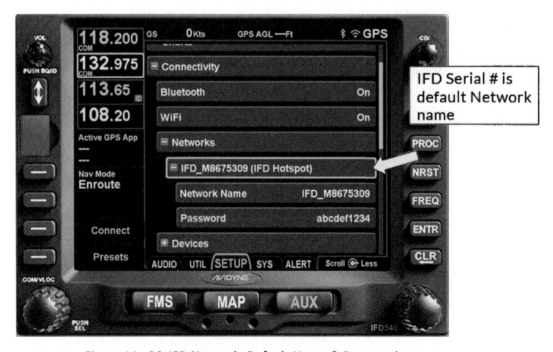

Figure 11 - 36 IFD Network- Default Name & Password

In this configuration, the IFD is acting as the WiFi hub. Let's connect our iPad to the IFD Hotspot. Go the Settings menu on your iPad and select Wif. Make sure the slider switch it set to On. You will then see a list of available nextworks. If you are out at your airplane, you will most likely have a limited number of choices. Look for the Network name of your IFD--in this case, "IFD_8675309". It will then prompt you for the password. Enter the default 10-digit password (abcedef1234) or your user-defined password if you have changed it. Your iPad will connect and you will see a check mark next to it like you see here.

Figure 11 - 37 Connecting iPad to IFD Network

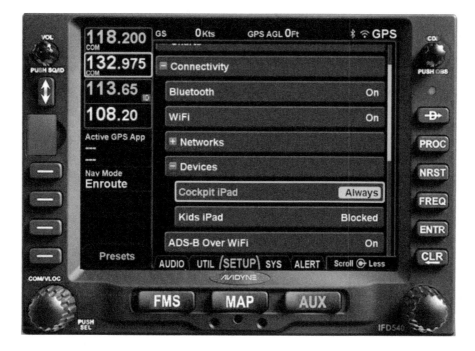

Figure 11 - 38 Devices - Enable the device(s) you want connected to your IFD.

Devices

As a security measure, any device that is trying to connect to the IFD network will appear under the Devices sub-category,   Each device listed will show the name or IP address of the device and the "connection policy" for that device. The connection policy controls whether the IFD will accept data transmitted by the device.

Connection policy options are as follows:

- Blocked – a device has made a request to connect to the IFD, but the pilot has not yet taken action to set the connection policy for the device

- Never – connection attempts by this device will automatically be rejected

- Once – this connection attempt will be accepted, but future connection attempts will require operator action to set the connection policy

- Always – connection attempts by this device will automatically be accepted By default, its connection policy will be set to "Blocked", and a "Connect Request" alert will be issued. Communication with the device will be inhibited until the pilot sets the connection policy to something other than "Blocked".

Figure 11 - 39 Request Message showing iPad trying to connect to your IFD.

If the device is trusted and will always be under control of the pilot, setting the connection policy to "Always" is appropriate. If the pilot prefers to specifically determine whether that device should be allowed on every connection attempt, the connection policy should be set to "Once". If this device is not known to the pilot, the connection policy should be set to "Never".

If the device is connected and the connection policy is set to "Always" or "Once", then the device name will be displayed in green. as shown in Fig 11-38.

In this example, we have set "Cockpit iPad" to "Always." The next time we go flying, the IFD will remember this iPad and you will not need to go through this full process again.

ADS-B Over Wifi

When the ADS-B Over WiFi selection is "On", the IFD will forward data received from a wired ADS-B In source over the WiFi interface. Most Electronic Flight Bag (EFB) applications will use this data to display weather and/or traffic. Some EFBs can be configured to get ADS-B data over other interfaces (e.g. Bluetooth). In those cases, this setting should be "Off". The factory default setting is "On". The ADS-B Over WiFi setting will only be shown if the IFD is configured to receive data from a wired ADS-B In source.

In this example, I have a SkyTrax200 ADS-B receiver hard-wired to my IFD, and I want the ADS-B traffic and weather to appear on my ForeFlight map and my IFD100 on my iPad, so I have enabled ADS-B over WiFi.

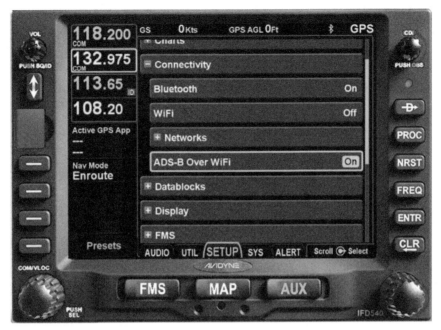

Figure 11 - 40 ADS-B Over WiFi Enabled.

What if I didnt have a SkyTrax200 ADS-B receiver, and instead I was flying with a compatible portable ADS-B device such as a Stratus3?

In that case, I would want my IFD and my iPad to connect to the Stratus 3 Network.   That means the IFD is no longer the network hub, it is a client on the Stratus3 network hub, as is the iPad.

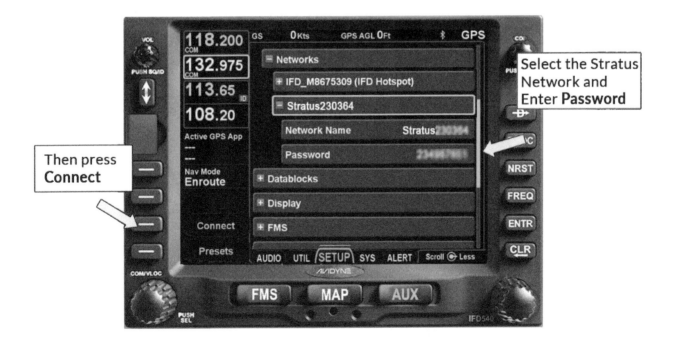

Figure 11 - 41 Connecting the IFD with a portable device such as a Stratus3

IFD440 and IFD410 Differences

Most of the features described in this lesson work the same way in the IFD440 and IFD410 as they do in the IFD5XX. However, since the IFD440/410's display is much smaller, there's no room for the left-side datablocks. That means that you can't place information on the left side of the display, and you can't have more than one standby frequency box.

Figure 11 - 42 IFD440 Datablocks

You can have just as many right-side datablocks on the IFD4XX as you can on the IFD5XX, but you can't see very many of them at the same time. That means you'll need to get creative.

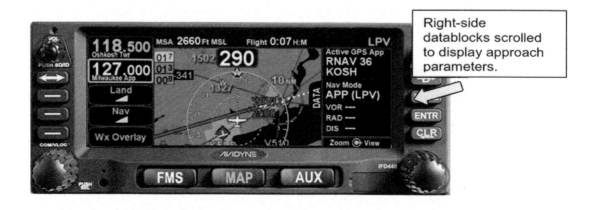

Figure 11 - 43 IFD440 Right Side Datablocks

One possible configuration would be to have a set of cruise datablocks and a set of approach datablocks, possibly separated with a blank datablock. The cruise datablocks would be displayed until you have started your approach. Then you would scroll to the approach datablocks. The important thing is to keep related datablocks together so you're not scrolling up and down all the time. Remember that the same datablock item can be placed in more than one spot. That means you can put information wherever it's needed.

Mini Flight Plan Format

Another FMS Setup function that is especially helpful on the IFD440/410 is the Mini Flight Plan Format, which allows you to see more flight plan waypoints on the smaller screen.   You can find this setting under the AUX->SETUP->FMS category, .

Figure 11 - 44 IFD440 Normal FMS Waypoint format on FMS FPL page

Figure 11 - 45 Selecting Mini Flight Plan Format

Figure 11 - 46 Mini Flight Plan Format on FMS FPL page

Lesson Review

This lesson looked at the information and utility features of the Avidyne IFD Series. The items that were covered are:

User Settings and Options

- The IFD can be customized with dozens of settings and options that can be tailored to the preferences of an individual pilot.

- Detailed information on each option can be found in the **Aux Subsystem** chapter of the IFD Pilot Guide.

Saving Settings for Individual Users

- Individual settings and options can be stored for up to ten different user profiles.

- The user profile currently in use is set by the User line select key (LSK 3) on the AUX SETUP tab.

- The user profile setting affects the Datablocks, Map Settings, FMS Settings, and User Options pages.

- The parameters saved on each of these pages will be automatically changed whenever a different user profile is selected.

- All changes to the affected options pages will be saved automatically under the user profile in use.

- The default user profiles are User 1, User 2, etc. They can be renamed as desired.

- Only letters and numbers can be used in user profile names.

Datablocks

- Datablocks are individual pieces of information that can be displayed on the top and right sides of the IFD5XX and IFD4XX screens.

- In addition, IFD5XXs can also display datablocks on the left side of the screen.

- Datablocks are completely configurable by the pilot. Each user profile can set up its own set of datablocks.

- Datablocks are set up on the AUX SETUP tab under the Datablocks category.

- The top set of datablocks contains two entries.

- The right set of datablocks can have over 25 entries. They can be scrolled up and down to bring different blocks into view.

- The left datablocks on the IFD5XX can be configured to contain up to nine datablocks or up to four standby frequency boxes and two datablocks.

- Datablocks can be returned to the factory settings using the Presets link select key (LSK1).

FMS Options

- The Setup FMS page controls the behavior of the IFD's internal flight management system.

- Some of the things that can be controlled here are:

    - Alerts for controlled airspace, special use airspace, and TFRs.

    - Flight plan access to airways, departures, arrivals, and approaches.

    - Mini Flight Plan format

- The FMS Options can be reset to the factory defaults by pressing and holding the IFD Multi-Function knob.

Map Options

- The display of features on the IFD moving map is controlled by going to the AUX SETUP tab and pressing the Setup Map line select key.

- The Airport Filter box on the Setup Map page controls the display of airports. Airports can be filtered by runway length, control tower, runway surface, and fuel availability.

- Airports that do not meet the filter criteria will not be displayed on the map and will not come up when the NRST key is pressed.

- The airport filter can be turned on and off when using the Nearest function by pressing the Filter On/ Off line select key on the NRST tab.

- The Map General box on the Map Setup page controls general settings. You can optimize the map feature display for IFR or VFR flight. You can also use your own custom settings or return to the factory defaults.

- The settings in the Map Detail box on the Map Setup page can be used to individually customize the display of each type of map feature. Each type can be set to be displayed at a specified zoom level, altitude, and setting of the decluttering button. Features can also be turned off completely.

- The Map Options can be reset to the factory defaults by pressing and holding the IFD Multi-Function knob.

Other User Options

- The AUX SETUP page includes several other User Options to set up a variety of parameters that affect the behavior of the IFD.

- Several of the more useful options include the Time Format, Switch Tanks Alert, and Approach settings.

- A complete description of all user options can be found in the **Map Subsystem** chapter of the IFD Pilot Guide.

- User options can be returned to their factory settings using the Presets link select key (LSK1) onthe AUX-> SETUP page.

Communication Frequency Presets

- The IFD can store up to sixteen preset communications frequencies.

- The preset frequencies can be accessed by pressing the Com Preset line select key on the AUX AUDIO tab.

- To use a preset frequency, go to the AUX AUDIO tab and press the Com Preset line select key. Then select the desired frequency. It will be transferred to the highlighted standby communications frequency box. Activate it by pressing the Frequency Swap key.

- Preset frequencies can also be selected by pressing an optional yoke-mounted button.

- To edit a preset frequency, go to the AUX AUDIO tab and press the Com Preset line select key. Then press the on-screen Edit button to make it turn blue. Then select and update the desired frequency.

Appendix A: IFD Quick Reference Guide

This appendix is an abbreviated summary of IFD procedures.
Refer to the main body of the text and to the Avidyne *IFDxxx Pilot's Guide* for complete information.

VHF Communication and Navigation

Tuning the Communication Radio

1. Press the center of the Com/Nav Tuning knob (if necessary) to display communications frequencies in the frequency boxes.

2. Turn the Com/Nav Tuning knob or tap on the frequency box and use the touch screen to enter the new communications frequency in the standby frequency box.

3. Press the Frequency Swap key to activate the new frequency.

Tuning the Navigation Radio

1. Press the center of the Com/Nav Tuning knob (if necessary) to display navigation frequencies in the frequency boxes.

2. Turn the Com/Nav Tuning knob or tap on the frequency box and use the touch screen to enter the new VOR or ILS frequency in the standby frequency box.

3. Press the Frequency Swap key to activate the new frequency.

Switching Between GPS and VHF Navigation Sources

1. Turn the CDI Source knob (upper right corner of IFD) to alternate between GPS and VLOC navigation mode.

2. The active mode is displayed in a green or yellow caption in the upper right corner of the IFD screen.

3. The aircraft position on the map display is always controlled by GPS, no matter which navigation source is selected. The navigation source mode only controls the left/right deviation signals sent to the navigation indicator.

Controlling Audio Volume

1. Select the radio to be controlled (com or nav) by pressing the center of the Com/Nav Tuning knob.

2. Turn the Volume/Power/Squelch/ID knob to set the radio volume.

3. The volume level is displayed as a green band underneath the frequency.

Turning Squelch On and Off

1. If necessary, select the com radio by pressing the center of the Com/Nav Tuning knob.

2. Turn the squelch on and off by pressing the center of the Volume/Power/Squelch/ID knob.

Turning the Nav ID Filter On and Off

1. If necessary, select the nav radio by pressing the center of the Com/Nav Tuning knob.

2. Turn the nav ID filter on and off by pressing the center of the Volume/Power/Squelch/ID knob.

3. When the nav ID filter is off the characters ID will appear in the navigation frequency box.

Quick-Tuning to the Emergency Frequency

1. Press and hold the Frequency Swap key for three seconds to tune to the 121.5 emergency frequency.

Building Flight Plans

Creating a New Flight Plan

1. Use the FMS rocker to display the FPL tab.

2. If no origin airport is displayed, press the ENTR key twice to bring up the origin airport entry box.

3. Use the touch screen or the IFD Multi-Function knob to enter the origin airport ID. Press ENTR to accept it.

4. Position the cyan insert cursor under the origin airport box.

5. Press the ENTR key enough times to bring up a new waypoint entry box.

6. Enter the ID of the next waypoint. Press the ENTR key to accept it.

7. Continue steps 4, 5, and 6 until all enroute waypoints are entered.

8. Enter the destination airport ID as the last waypoint.

9. Activate the new flight plan by pressing the Activate line select key.

10. A green GPS caption will appear in the upper right corner of the IFD display if there is an active flight plan leg and the IFD is receiving a valid GPS navigation signal.

Reviewing a Flight Plan

1. All flight plans should be thoroughly reviewed before use.

2. Flight plans can be reviewed graphically on the FMS FPL tab by tapping on the vertical MAP tab to display a split screen showing a map on the left and the flight plan on the right.

3. Use the outer IFD Multi-Function knob to scroll through the entire flight plan, checking each waypoint.

4. Use the View Cursor line select key to see each waypoint graphically as you scroll.

Adding a Waypoint to a Flight Plan

1. Use the FMS rocker to display the FPL tab.

2. Place the cyan insert cursor between the two waypoints where the new waypoint is to be added.

3. Press the ENTR key enough times to bring up a new waypoint entry box.

4. Enter the ID of the new waypoint. Press the ENTR key to accept it.

Deleting a Flight Plan Waypoint

1. Use the FMS rocker to display the FPL tab.

2. Place the cyan edit cursor box over the waypoint to be deleted.

3. Press the CLR key.

4. If necessary, press the ENTR key to confirm the deletion.

Adding an Airway to the Flight Plan

1. Use the FMS rocker to display the FPL tab.

2. Add the airway entry point waypoint to the flight plan if it's not there already.

3. While the cyan insert cursor is positioned after the entry waypoint, press the ENTR key to display a list of airways.

4. Select the desired airway. Press the ENTR key to confirm.

5. A list of exit point waypoints will appear. Select the appropriate one and press the ENTR key to confirm.

6. Check the airway's waypoints to ensure that they are correct.

Adding a Standard Departure to a Flight Plan

1. Use the FMS rocker to display the FPL tab.

2. Add the origin airport to the flight plan if it's not there already.

3. Select the Rnwy box of the origin airport. Press the ENTR key to display a runway list.

4. Select the departure runway and press the ENTR key to confirm it.

5. Select the Departure box of the origin airport. Press the ENTR key to display a list of departures.

6. Select the departure and press the ENTR key to confirm it.

7. A list of departure transitions may be displayed. If so, select the appropriate one and press the ENTR key to confirm it.

8. If the departure runway changes, make sure to change it in the flight plan and ensure that the proper departure procedure has been selected.

9. Always check the departure procedure to ensure that it contains the correct waypoints.

Adding a Standard Arrival to a Flight Plan

1. Use the FMS rocker to display the FPL tab.

2. Add the destination airport to the flight plan if it's not there already.

3. Select the Arr box of the arrival airport and press the ENTR key.

4. Select the arrival and press ENTR to confirm it.

5. If necessary, select the appropriate transition and press ENTR to confirm it.

6. When the arrival runway is known, enter it in the Rnwy box of the destination airport waypoint.

7. Always program the standard arrival and the arrival runway before you program the instrument approach procedure.

8. Always check the arrival procedure to ensure that it contains the correct waypoints.

Deleting the Current Flight Plan

1. Use the FMS rocker to go to the FMS ROUTE page.

2. Select the Current route box.

3. Press the CLR key.

4. Press the ENTR key to confirm the route deletion.

Saving and Retrieving Flight Plans

Saving a Flight Plan for Later Use

1. Use the FMS rocker to display the FMS ROUTE page.

2. Select the Current Route box.

3. Press the Copy line select key.

4. Enter the route's name in the Name box.

5. Press the Back to Route List line select key to go back to the list of saved routes.

Activating a Saved Flight Plan

1. Use the FMS rocker to display the FMS ROUTE page.

2. Select the route to be activated.

3. Press the Activate Route line select key.

4. Press the ENTR key to confirm the route activation.

Inverting a Saved Flight Plan

1. Use the FMS rocker to display the FMS ROUTE page.

2. Select the route to be inverted.

3. Press the Invert line select key.

4. Enter the route's name in the Name box.

5. Press the Back to Route List line select key to go back to the list of saved routes.

Deleting a Saved Flight Plan

1. Use the FMS rocker to display the FMS ROUTE page.

2. Select the route to be deleted.

3. Press the CLR key.

4. Press the ENTR key to confirm the route deletion.

Flying a Flight Plan

Flight Leg Depiction on the MAP Tab

1. The current leg is depicted in magenta.

2. The next leg is a magenta barber pole.

3. Previous and subsequent legs are white.

Going Direct to a Waypoint on the Current Flight Plan

1. Use the FMS rocker to display the FPL tab.

2. Select the waypoint to go to direct to.

3. Press the Direct-To key.

4. Press the ENTR key twice to confirm.

Going Direct to a Waypoint Not on the Current Flight Plan

1. Press the Direct-To key.

2. Enter the ID of the new waypoint in the Direct-To dialog box.

3. Press the ENTR key twice to confirm.

4. Use the FMS rocker to display the FPL tab.

5. Review the flight plan and clean up any gaps that have been created.

Intercepting a Radial from a Waypoint

1. Use the FMS rocker to display the FPL tab.

2. Select the waypoint you want to navigate to.

3. Press the Activate Leg line select key and then confirm your selection by pressing the ENTR key.

4. Press the OBS knob to put the IFD into OBS mode.

5. Select the desired TO radial with the course selector of your HSI or navigation indicator.

Offsetting a Flight Plan Leg

1. Use the FMS rocker to display the FPL tab.

2. Select the waypoint at the end of the current leg.

3. Press the Offset Route line select key.

4. Use the IFD Multi-Function knob to set an offset distance. Offsets right or left of course can be selected.

5. Press the ENTR key to confirm the offset.

Cancelling a Flight Plan Leg Offset

1. Use the FMS rocker to display the FPL tab.
2. Select the waypoint at the end of the current leg.
3. Press the Offset Route line select key.
4. Press the Delete Offset line select key.

Graphically Adding a New Waypoint with Rubber Band Mode

1. Use the MAP rocker to display the MAP page.
2. Place your finger on the leg to be rubber-banded for at least two seconds. The leg will turn cyan.
3. Use your finger to drag it to the position where a new waypoint is to be inserted.
4. Confirm the new waypoint by pressing ENTR. Reject it by pressing CLR.
5. Use the Direct button to go direct to the new waypoint if desired.

Holding Patterns

Adding a Holding Pattern to a Flight Plan

1. Use the FMS rocker to display the FPL tab.
2. Position the cyan insert cursor after the holding waypoint.
3. Press the ENTR key and select the Hold at xxxx option.
4. Press the ENTR key again to accept the hold.
5. Review the holding pattern parameters to ensure they are correct. If necessary, change the holding course, the turn direction, and the leg length of the hold to the desired values.

Deleting a Holding Pattern

1. Use the FMS rocker to display the FPL tab.
2. Place the cyan edit cursor box on the holding pattern.
3. Press the CLR key.
4. It is not good practice to delete a holding pattern after the aircraft has entered it. The hold should be exited instead.

Exiting a Holding Pattern

There are three ways to exit a holding pattern:

1. Go direct to another waypoint.
2. Press the Exit Hold line select key. This will cause the IFD to complete the current circuit around the hold and exit when it crosses the holding fix.
3. Go direct to the holding waypoint, then delete the holding pattern. This will cause the IFD to turn to the holding fix and then exit the hold.

Instrument Approaches

Selecting an Instrument Approach

1. Set up the complete flight plan, including the destination airport.

2. Press the PROC key to display a list of approaches. If there is more than one destination airport, press the PROC key multiple times until approaches for the correct destination are displayed.

3. Select the desired approach from the list. Press the ENTR key to confirm.

4. Select the desired transition. Press the ENTR key to confirm.

5. Review the entire flight plan and close any gaps that have been introduced.

6. If a vectors to final transition has been selected, press the Activate Approach line select key on the FMS FPL page when you are cleared for the approach.

Procedure for Instrument Approaches

The standard procedure for an instrument approach is:

1. When the landing runway and the approach in use is known, program the IFD with the expected approach and its transition.

2. When cleared by ATC, go direct to the approach fix or activate the appropriate leg of the approach.

3. Confirm the approach minimums from the approach chart that correspond to the expected navigation source state displayed on the IFD.

4. As the approach proceeds, confirm that:

    a. The IFD transitions from ENRT to TERM to APP navigation mode.

    b. The appropriate VOR or localizer frequency is auto-tuned (if applicable),

    c. The appropriate course is set on the HSI or navigation indicator.

    d. The appropriate navigation source state (GPS or VLOC) is displayed in the navigation source state window.

5. At the missed approach point, apply power, re-configure the aircraft for climb, and confirm that the IFD has automatically transitioned to the missed approach procedure and GPS navigation state.

6. If the approach used a vector to final transition, press the Retry Approach line select key to reload the approach for another attempt.

Procedure Turns and Course Reversals

1. Course reversals will be automatically included in instrument approaches unless a NoPT or vectors to final transition is selected.

2. Holding pattern course reversals can be deleted from approaches, but procedure turns cannot be.

3. Use the normal holding pattern delete procedure to delete a holding pattern course reversal.

4. To skip a procedure turn go direct to another approach waypoint or by activate the leg after the procedure turn.

Appendix B: Where to Find It

This appendix is a quick reference of where to find commonly used IFD utilities and settings.

Airport, Navaid, and Facility Information

What It Is	Where to Find It

Airport Information
    General
    Communications
    Approaches
    Weather
	FMS INFO tab

Navaid Information
    Frequency
    Location
    Weather
	FMS INFO tab

Nearest
    Airports
    VORs
    NDBs
    Intersections
    ARTCCs
    FSSs
    User Waypoints
    Special use airspaces
	FMS NRST tab, line select to appropriate facility type
	or
	NRST key (IFD5XX only), line select to appropriate facility type

Airport and facility search	FMS INFO tab, Search line select key

IFD Software, Database, and Datalink Status

What It Is	Where to Find It
IFD software status	AUX SYS tab, Status Software line select key
IFD Serial Number	AUX SYS tab, Status Software line select key
GPS and WAAS status	AUX SYS tab, Status GPS line select key
Navigation, chart, terrain, and obstacle database status	AUX SYS tab, Status Databases line select key
Datalink status	AUX SYS tab, Status Datalink line select key

Timers, Calculators, and Checklists

What It Is	Where to Find It

Timers
    Generic
    Trip Timer
    Departure time
    Custom
	AUX UTIL tab, Timers line select key

Calculators
    Air data
    Fuel planner
    Trip planner
    RAIM
    Trip statistics
    Weight Calculator
	AUX UTIL tab, Calculators line select key

Checklists	AUX UTIL tab, Checklists line select key

IFD Configuration and Settings

What It Is	Where to Find It
Controlled Airspace Alerts TFR Alerts SUA Alerts Transition Altitude/Level Alerts Switch Tanks Alert Top of Descent Alert Airspace Aural Waypoint Aural	AUX SETUP tab - +Alerts
Charts Day/Night Mode Chart Auto Mode	AUX SETUP tab - +Charts
Bluetooth WiFi Networks Devices ADS-B over WiFi	AUX SETUP tab - +Connectivity
Datablock Setup	AUX SETUP tab - +Datablocks
Map Orientation Airport Filter Altitude Filter Compass Rose Heading Box	AUX SETUP tab- +Map
Com Frequency Spacing Auto-LOC tuning Auto GPS-->VLOC Capture	AUX SETUP tab,- +Radio

VNAV Transition Altitude Transistion Level high Altitude Airways Low Altidude Airwary Arrivals Departures Approaches Visual Approaches Patterns SBAS Channel Numbers Mini flight Plan Format Advisory Glideslope Auto Enabled Missed	AUX SETUP tab- +FMS
Terrain Awareness (TA) Terrain Caution Aural Terrain Warning Aural FLTA Exclusion Areas	AUX SETUP tab,- +Terrain
UTC Local Time Offset Time Format Local Time	AUX SETUP tab- +Time
Bearing Reference Distance/Speed Units Altitude/VS Units Pressure Units Temperature Units Fuel Units Position Units	AUX SETUP tab- +Units
User Profiles	AUX SETUP tab - +User Profiles

Appendix C: Datablock Contents Guide

This appendix provides an alphabetic list of the contents of each datablock and its corresponding name.

Datablocks can be displayed on the left (IFD5XX only), top, and right sides of the IFD display.

Datablock Contents	Datablock Name
Altitude – GPS AGL	GPS AGL Altitude
Altitude – minimum safe	Minimum Safe Altitude
Approach – Active GPS	Active GPS Approach
Blank line	*** Blank ***
Comm radio frequencies	Com/Nav Standby #n
Course deviation indicator, current track, and desired track	GPS CDI
Cross track distance	Cross Track Distance
Designated waypoint identifier, bearing, radial, distance, and estimated time enroute	Designated waypoint information (waypoint can be set by user)
Desired track	Desired Track
Desired track for the next flight plan leg	Next Desired Track
Destination ID and estimated time enroute	Destination ETE
Destination ID and estimated time of arrival	ETA at Dest
Destination identifier	Destination Waypoint
Destination identifier and straight line distance	Direct Distance to Dest.
Destination identifier, direct bearing and distance	Dest Direct Info
Destination identifier, distance along the remaining flight plan legs, estimated fuel, and estimated time enroute	Dest Along Track Info

Fuel amount remaining	Fuel Amount Remaining
Fuel flow	Fuel Flow
Fuel miles per gallon	Fuel Economy
Fuel time remaining	Fuel Time Remaining
Fuel used	Fuel Used
Ground speed	Ground Speed
Ground track	Ground Track
ILS ID, airport, and runway	Decoded VLOC IDENT
Lat/lon position	Aircraft Position
Nav radio frequencies	VLOC Radio
Navigation mode	Navigation Mode
Nearest airport ID, bearing, and distance	Nearest Airport
Next waypoint identifier, track along flight plan route, distance, fuel, and estimated time enroute	Next waypoint information
Number of active warnings, alerts, and caution messages	Number of Alerts
Outside air temperature	OAT
Radar Altitude - Feet	Radar Altitude
Static Air Temperature	SAT
Time – local	Local Time
Time – UTC	UTC Time
Time in flight	Flight Timer

Appendix C: Datablock Contents Guide

Index

Index

Printed in Great Britain
by Amazon

32830852R00163